P9-BZS-625

Copyright © 1974 by Happiness Press
All rights reserved. This book or parts
thereof may not be reproduced in any form
without written permission of the publishers.

Library of Congress Card Number 74-21034

Other Happiness Press Books:

The First Book of Do-in (1971)
Do-in and Acupuncture Wall Atlas
Acupuncture and the Philosophy of the Far East
Food for Spiritual Development
Kuzu, the Healing Root
Cooking Good Food
Cooking with Grains And Vegetables

Recording in Cassette form of the
full instruction and text from
the Second Book of Do-in is available.

In preparation:

Survival First Aid
Water, Salt and Bread as Cosmic Elements
Baby Do-in and the New Age Child

For information, see your bookseller
or address: Happiness Press
160 Wycliff Way, Magalia, Ca. 95954

The Art of Rejuvenation through Self-massage and Breathing exercises

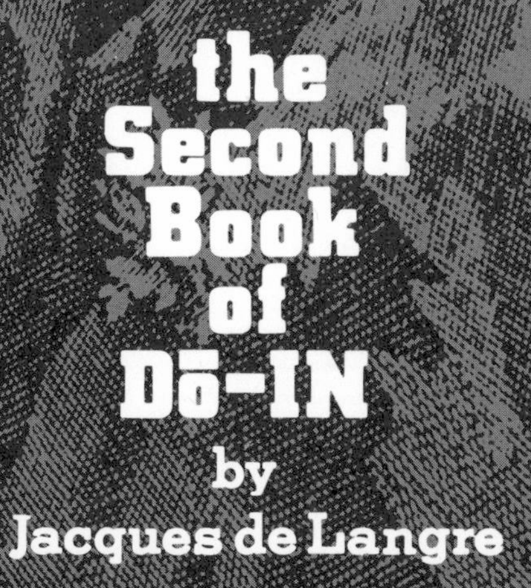
the
Second
Book
of
Dō-IN
by
Jacques de Langre

to my wife Yvette
my constant
Inspiration
and
Eternal Mate

TABLE OF CONTENTS

Foreword

Change is Inevitable . . .

. . . our resisting it will cause our own destruction.

For an evaluation and further description of the druidic Do-in practices, see page 10, 33 and the actual exercises in the second part of this book.

In the face of the approaching crisis for man and earth, a concern for the survival of both has urged me to write this book. This is the manual of self-government for positive reconstruction of man's body for those who truly will, to pass whole through the impending change.

The superior man understands change in order to live in harmony. He flows with that change and does not oppose it in any way. Are human beings living in the present kind of body, with today's state of mind, capable of performing within the change or will the present humans be so inflexible and attached to outdated material values, that they will be superseded?

As our part of the cosmos moves toward something else, within the old civilization a new one is already stirring, with some hesitant probing, unfamiliar shapes and concepts. But ultimately new economic, social and human structures will emerge. Along with this trend to truer values, a return to very ancient metaphysical practices is apparent.

The dominant characteristic of this new age of man is an overwhelming urge for individual self-awareness. This begins with the realization that:

"Illness is the result of alienation
from the natural Order of the Universe."

Those of us who understand this, strive for a restoration of the natural order in and around ourselves. Most ancient and almost forgotten, Do-in definitely has a place in this change.*

*For a more detailed discussion, see "Beyond Do-in" chapter.

The Scientific Basis of Do-in - Myth or Medical Reality

Restoring all of the body's functions by a few intuitive percussions, pressures and fingertip massages smacks of being another "empirical remedy". At best, it is met with polite scepticism by the modern scientific mind.

A universal trait of medical practitioners is to keep well informed on new remedies. The layman of the western world is also curious about alternate methods of healing, especially when disappointed by the scientific cures, once regarded as infallible. However, both physician and patient demand to see "scientific proof" of the ancient traditional medicines before trying them.

My search for proofs found even greater helpers among the very descendants of the originators of Do-in, for when these orientals become doctors of medicine in western colleges, their scepticism regarding these ancient healing arts clamors for even more irrefutable proofs.

There is a close relationship between acupuncture and Do-in. --Both use identical skin acupoints and possess identical theories on the origin and the cure of diseases-- This similarity helped my task of validating Do-in's effectiveness by proving the scientific basis of the first.

Astrology and Do-in

Astrology departs from Astronomy in one major direction: While both deal with the same objects of "Time and its Cycles", the aim of the first is to interpret the meaning of these cycles with reference to the opportunities for harmony, composure, health and growth in individuals.

In its highest and most practical function, the astrological science never deals with cosmic fate, but with the possibilities, which each man has, to fully participate in the harmonious cosmic cycle.

To realize this synchronized harmony with the cosmos is to achieve a state of wholeness, balance, health, and a sense of well-being. All ancient teachings include the many ways to reach or to restore such a state. The value of Do-in breathing exercises is greatly increased when they are performed in accordance, awareness and harmony with the day-night, lunation and seasonal cycles.

In the Orient, astrology was identified not only with religion but also with the Tao's astrological lore which states: ". . . the living force of the whole universe is also that of man." Since the air was considered full of "The Seeds of Life", breathing was considered of utmost importance.

In this 15th century woodcut, constellations are shown in their positions regulating and ruling the human body's vital organs.

Early Taoist magicians believed that deities lived in every part of the human body, they were gods of the sky, the earth, the constellations, mountains and rivers. Breathing exercises and meditation made it possible to not only feel these cosmic deities, but to obtain from them spiritual and physiological rules guidance relating to health. It was then known that the organism could be purified by Do-in: Taking air, water and sun baths which would pervade the body with celestial influences and by the abstinence from unpure foods.

It matters little whether astrology has been proven to rule man's fate or only his state of well-being. What matters is that "When man allows cosmic forces (earth, sea and sky energies) to enter and regulate his body and his consciousness in tune with the astrobiological rhythms; his life takes on the regularity, the harmony and the orderliness of the omnipotent infinite world."

Applying this precept to the practice of Do-in, the practitioner soon sees that his own body rhythms and those of each organ within him respond strongly to a biological clock ruled by forces of nature. Three meaningful astrobiological rhythms having a proven influence – authenticated by modern research-- on the life and health of man, will be studied here, for they help to understand Do-in in a practical way.

The contemporary science of chronobiology: Each of our bodily functions submit to a maximum and a minimum rhythm, has confirmed the periodicity of these cycles by many successful experiments.

Thermodynamic and biophysical laws formulate the concept of an energy having different aspects depending on the energy level fluctuating with the various moments of the cycle. The principle of a "Circulating Energy" has been made evident by a most modern and fundamental work on "Pathogenic Bioenergetic" written by Dr. Nguyen Van Nghi, M.D. Recent discovery of the proof of this circulation of energy and its constant equilibrium shows that an unbalance or an interruption of this flow is a prime cause of disease.

Bioastrology studies the effects of celestial influence on life and health. Biocosmology is a branch of biology studying the relationship between planets and their effect on the life and health of man. Understanding how these planets affect our biological rhythms is important for the effective practice of Do-in.

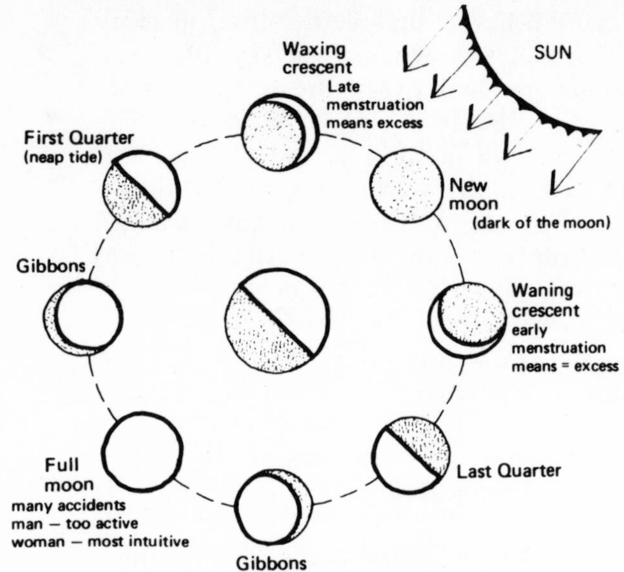

The moon and its phases, affecting all life on earth in a multitude of ways.

The combined pulling force of the sun and the moon on the earth may appear, at first study, as insignificant. The tidal pull moves, not only the whole body of the oceans, but the earth's crust also breathes with a rise -- at Spring tides -- of about six inches and the gaseous atmospheric blanket that surrounds the earth swells out to a distance of many miles, toward the moon and the sun.

This gravitational pull on the large body of salt water has a similar influence on our body's mass of plasma. Quantitatively, this pull can only be measured in a loss of a fraction of an ounce at each fall of the tide. The bioelectrogenesis effect is a little more important: The production of electricity by man's organism; as well as the biodynamic influence: The energy or "activity" measurement of our living organism is considerably affected by the cosmic pull.*

The daily journey of the moon around the earth creates a bulge of all oceans on the side of the earth facing the moon. In spite of its much larger size, the sun, much farther away, has a tidal effect about half that of the moon. However, when sun, moon and earth are in direct line, as in the full and new moon, both planets add their pull and cause unusually high tides -- Spring tides.-- When moon-earth and sun-earth lines are at right angle to each other -- Moon's first and third quarters --, the pull of these planets partly cancel each other out, resulting in low or neap tides.

Regardless of whether we live near the ocean or in the mountains, these complex solar and lunar gravitational pulls influence our biological function in many ways. Disturbances and alterations of hormonal flow as well as a decrease in the formation of red blood cells has been linked to the moon phases. In Switzerland, when the Foehn blows -- warm, dry wind descending the northern slopes of the Alps -- no surgical operations are ever performed since patients never recover. This is now part of a study made on the effects of climate and micro-climate on the life of plants and men.

Moon's gravitational pull on earth is twice that of the sun.

The waxing moon's real influence on earth's life aspects is easily discerned in the behaviour of the epileptics, schizophrenics, psychopaths and other sufferers from nervous dis-

*When the moon is full, one should not tonify (One should CALM). At the time of the new moon, one should not CALM (One should tonify). See Chapter on "Inductive Massage."

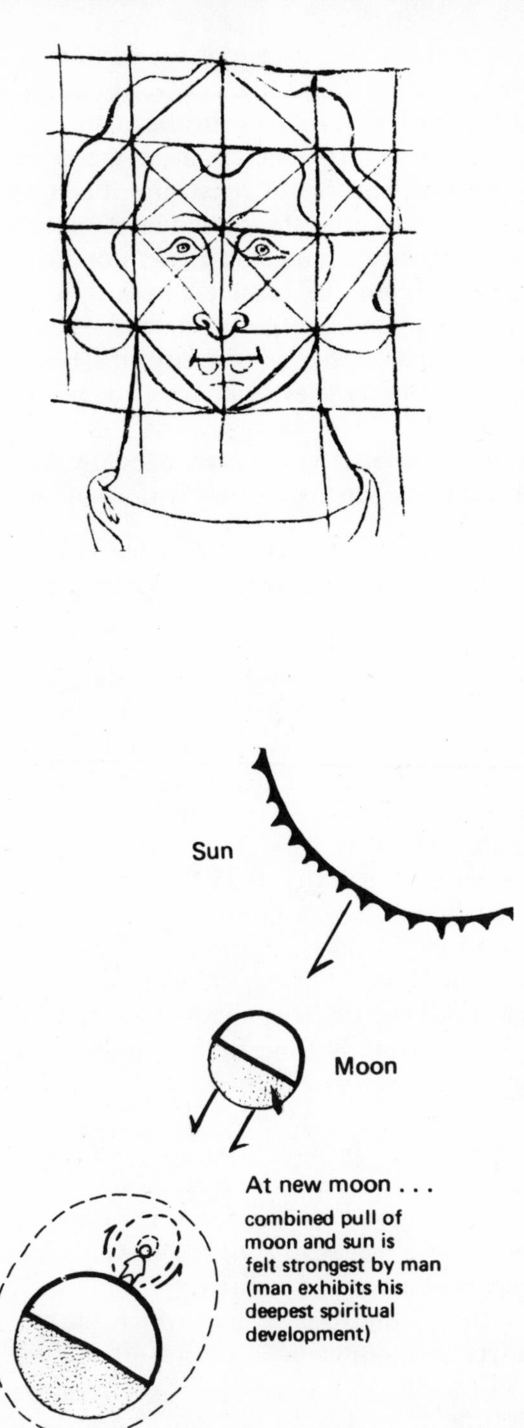

orders – sometimes referred to as "lunatics". – Sudden deaths and delinquency are also on the rise at the time of the moon's first quarter up to the full moon.

Solar spots are followed by significant variation of earth temperature, storms and even cyclones. For man, pathological troubles increase in severity when the spots are active, large and numerous.

The influential properties of outer space vary constantly. As individuals – depending on our state of body, mind, plasma, DNA and nervous system condition – we are also affected differently. While all men, collectively, in the same local area or time zone, receive the same planetary influence (66% from the moon and 33% from the sun), their receptivity and reaction to the cosmic forces depend also somewhat on their individual make up. Could it be that the rising of the moon at night intimates to us that here is the most propitious time for rest, a time to shelter our nervous system from the overstimulation of the nocturnal planet? Is it not surprising that bedtime Do-in traditionally consists of exercises designed to damper our nervous system? The greatest stimulation, by far, is the day and night cycle with the sunrise marking the strongest impelling force, pulling man's body from the night's inactivity and energizing him for a day of performance. The most spectacular changes in state of health is always noticed in those individuals who perform Do-in at sunrise.

Bioclimatology also takes into consideration the effects of light and darkness on living beings. This science has proven that many more accidents occur and that man becomes hyperactive at the time of the full moon. In contrast his woman companion becomes most intuitive at full moon but further the female is influenced in her menstruations by the phases of lunar energy. This particular facet of biological rhythms is well-known in oriental medicine where two pressure points in the acupressure system are used to bring the menstrual flow back into harmony with the moon.*

Further division of the 24 hour day into 12 segments of celestial influence on the various body organs is an accepted fact in the oriental philosophy of medicine. The western world is not ready to accept this concept without proofs. I am now prepared to offer a substantial evidence based on scientific analysis:

*See the chapter: "Menstruation" for acupoints and their particular influence.

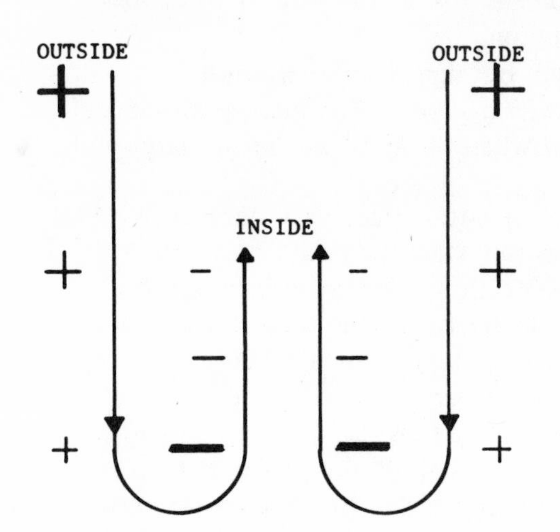

Any vertical entity standing on the surface of the earth may be considered as an antenna, presenting a higher polarity at the top than at the base. A human body follows this law and possesses a constant polarity with a higher potential at the head than at the feet. While this potential is not constant -- it is subject to variations in the same way everything else that is cycled around us and within us -- it always retains a higher potential at the top. This body polarity could be named "Physical Polarity" and forms the underlying basis of our electromagnetic make up. In conjunction with this physical polarity, the body possesses a "Physiological Polarity" evident in two ways.

a. Each organ possesses a bipolar metabolism obeying biorhythms, the potential level of each paired off with another.

b. An outside-inside relationship where the outside always remains positive and the inside, negative in comparison.

Thus, each paired organs have a high-low physical polarity with a cyclic and variable potential override, linked to the metabolic function of the group studied but also dependant on the cosmic and terrestial biorhythms. As a concrete example, let us study the energêtic polarity of the group, Small Intestine - (from the hand to the head) -- Bladder - (from the head to the foot). Readily, we see that the first half of the group, Small Intestine, is at a higher level of polarity than Bladder. Therefore a physiological polarity will have a downward movement, positive to negative, toward the Bladder. However, having reached the lowermost part of the body, this potential wave is now negative in regard to the top. This results in a movement toward the opposite polarity: A flow from bottom to the top. But this return must take place in an adjacent circuit whose polarity is opposite to that of the first one.

A potential impulse from top to bottom is positive and transverses the external -- positive -- zone of the body. Reaching the bottom -- negative polarity in regard to the top -- the impulse must follow an internal zone -- negative -- of the body, being impelled to the top which is of a positive polarity.

The movement of matter in the form of ions which fill our body and have their origin in the metabolic process of organs, also fall under the laws of polarity: External-positive, internal-negative; As well as flowing from top to bottom. A constant movement of these ions within, the negative-charged, produced

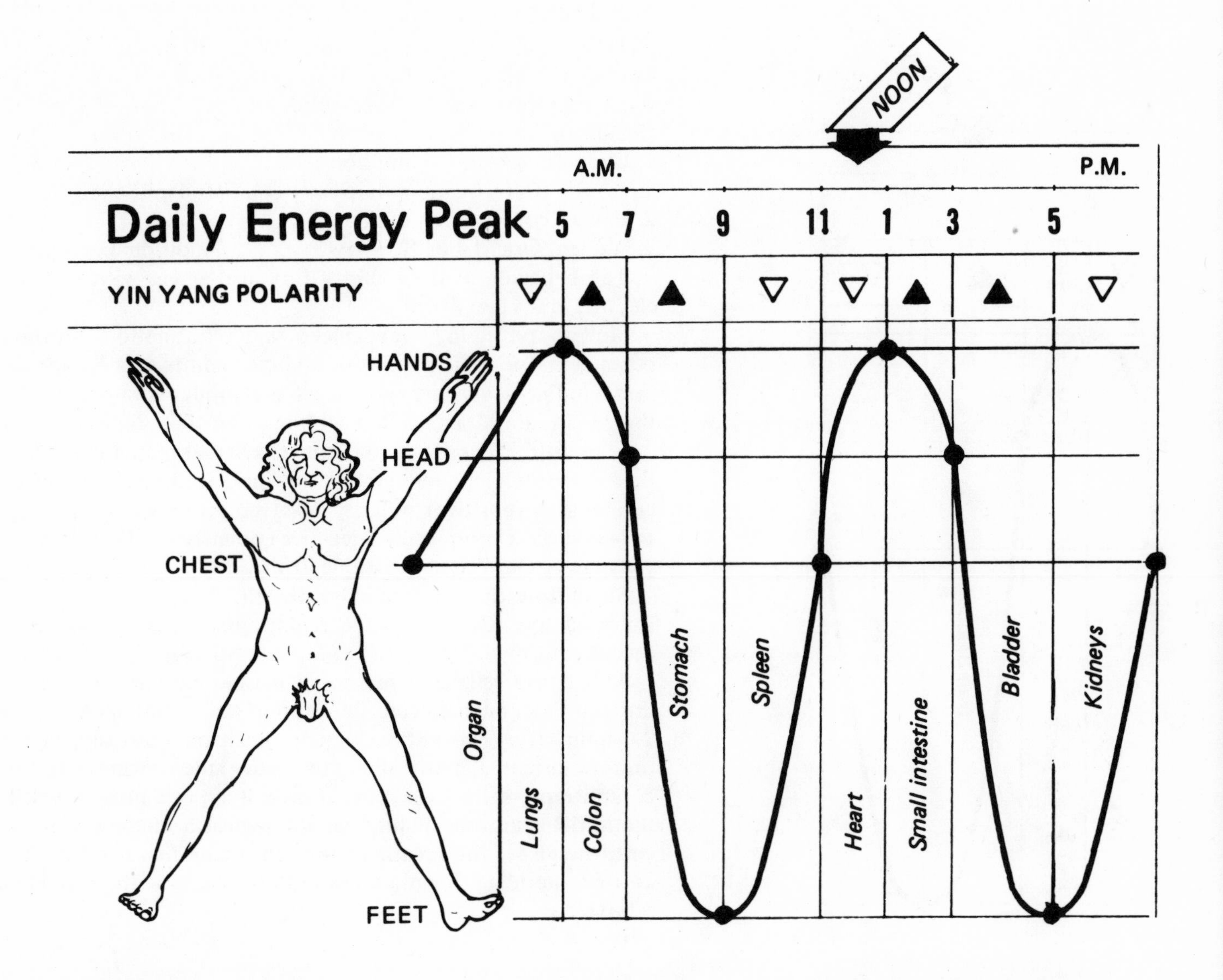

Traditional Oriental Medicine

. . . for each meridian, there is a two-hour period in every twenty four hour day when the high wave of activity makes it more receptive to stimulation. The surge of Ki flow or high wave last two hours; the superior physician finds it advisable to treat the meridian of a weakened organ at the beginning of the two hour period of flow surge.

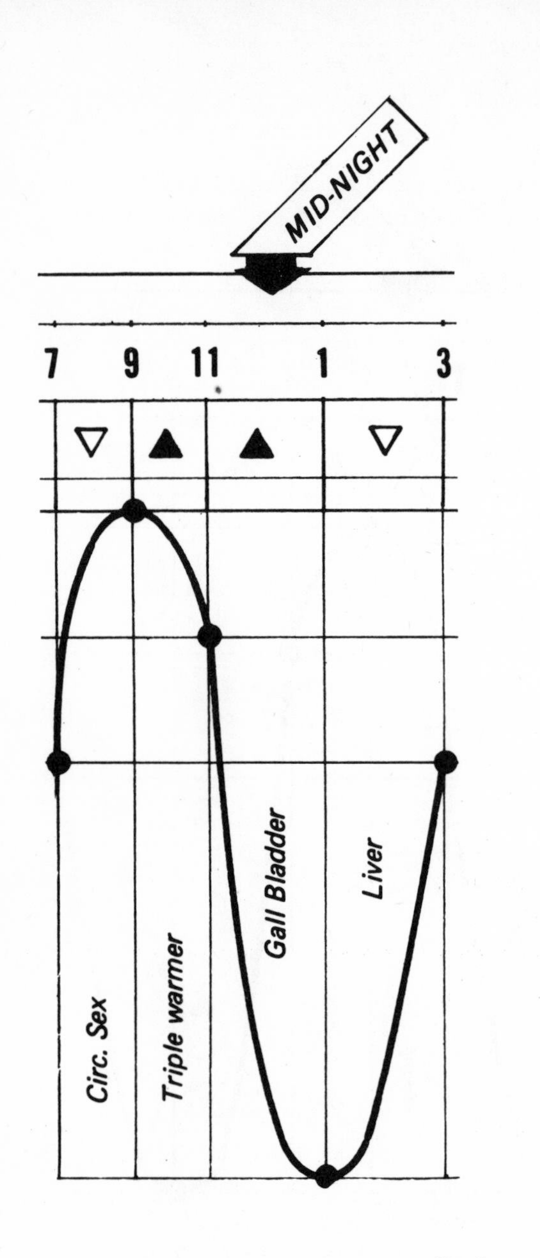

at the center will gravitate toward the exterior surface and conversely the positive, formed externally, will move toward the depths of the internal core.

This constant fluctuation from the top to the bottom and its reverse as well as the flow from external to internal and vice-versa conforms exactly to three recognized physical/physiological laws:

1. Electromagnetic Conduction Law (Carrying of an impulse) — Modern Scientific
2. Law of conservation of energy
3. Ancient Oriental Ki flow law — Traditional, empirical

The behavior of the polarity flux also agrees with the "Bio-electrogenesis law."

Modern physiology recognizes that all functions are interdependent for their precise periodicity and have a "computerized" in-line sequence, with each metabolic wave triggered by the preceeding one and itself inciting the following one.

Therefore, if we study the entire schematic circuit of the Ki flow and single out one circulation unit, it always consists of a complete + (positive) polarity level group of two yang organs followed by a complete – (negative) polarity level group of two yin organs. Our framed example at the left:

Small Intestine and Bladder for the Yang group (positive) followed by: Kidneys and Circulation/sex for the yin group (negative).

This entire scientific reasoning meshes exactly with the traditional oriental medicine concept of the 12 segments in the 24 hour day. The entire human organism possessing a continuous circuit, symetrical and repetitive; the starting point may be arbitrarily set anywhere. However, it appears proper to select the initial symptom of birth as the logical beginning of the circuit, therefore, the breath or the lungs meridian has been used as first meridian for the past 5,000 years by the traditional school.

Do-in Early Form

Paleontology has proven that Stone-Age man knew the practical aspects of self-management, self healing and even used flint needles and bird bones on occasion, in an attempt to cure his arthritic deformities.

Skeletal remains of Pithecanthropus man, -- excavated and examined by the Dutch doctor and paleontologist, Dubois, in Java – possessed on his thigh bone, swellings which were diag-

nosed as tumor.

At the beginning of the Quaternary Ice Age, 500,000 years ago, skeletal remains proved that Neanderthal man often suffered from chronic arthritis. In the Old Stone Age, the ancestor of Homo Sapiens was plagued by such bone diseases as spinal tuberculosis, sinusitis and osteomyelitis.

These discoveries made nonsense of the theory that when man lived in a natural state there was no illness present. But it does mean that early man, directed by a purer instinct, knew better how to cope with his ailments with many forms of self-care and self-cure developed out of the necessity for survival.

The study of the ancient medicines of all countries also shows a universal trait: When living conditions bring a reduction of hard physical labor; ritual breathing exercises are performed, mostly in groups, in order to effectively maintain a high level of flexibility, Ki flow and health.

We further notice that, invariably, when an ethnic group retains a high level of body mobility while, at the same time, respecting astrobiological life rhythms, it appears to maintain higher judgement and live more peacefully, in far better harmony and happiness than its more sedentary neighbors.

Metaphysical Mechanism of Do-in

If we define metaphysics as the science of the inward and the essential nature of things, apart from the common mode of thoughts, we can readily see that Do-in will appeal mainly to those individuals who wish to remain in harmony with nature, at some cost of disharmony with the modern world and its routine comfort. Often, metaphysical sciences will offer concepts which pertain to unverifiable hypothesis. This is as it should be: Let the common man brand this knowledge as unproven or hermetical because it is that same secrecy of metaphysics which enabled these sciences to remain pure and effective, giving the initiate an absolute might, beyond the power of the common man.

Secret Power of Dō-in

The secret power of Do-in is that it puts man in harmony with the motion of the universe, setting him "in tune" with the infinite . . .

A person who has mastered Do-in, acquires within himself the vibrations of the universe and can say: "I am the Universe". Then, if anyone or anything outside of this person, tries to disrupt, upset or attack him; this outsider, having pitted his force against the harmony of the universe, fails. If illness or anything negative tries to strike one who is "One with the Universe", in order to succeed, it would first have to break the harmony of the Universe.

When we demonstrate Do-in to others, we devotedly protect all beings in a spirit of reconstruction and reconciliation which permits everyone to accomplish his supreme mission.

> **Nicht fort sollst Du dich pflanzen,**
> **sonder hinauf.**
> **Dazu helfe dir der Garten der Ehe**
>
> Friedrich Wilhelm Nietzche 1844-1900
> "Die Frohlische Wissenschaft"

The Supreme Function of Do-in

The secret powers of Do-in, as outlined on the opposite page certainly qualifies this discipline as esoterical. Esoterical science is defined as: ". . . encompassing all of the secrets of nature," and is further described as follows: ". . . endowed with this knowledge, the initiate possesses an absolute might, beyond the power of the common man."

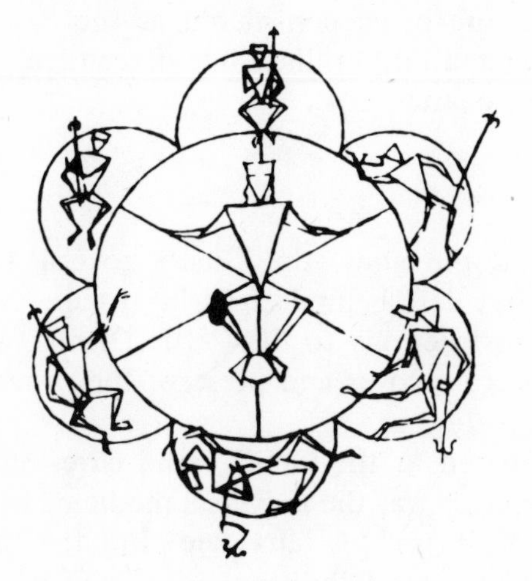

In its higher function, Do-in is a means to participate to the building of the human family, not primarily to correct others but to enlighten and correct our own spirit and body. German philosopher Nietzche must have had this supreme function in mind when he wrote the above.

The strictly mechanical practice of Do-in has often worked improvements on major physical defects and even on organic functional deficiencies since the daily routine of breathing exercises alone will insure a more orderly flow of Ki through the organs and bring a more stable harmony to the body. While it is true that an understanding of how this works is not of prime importance - since the flow of energy does not depend on and is much older than the labels placed on the functions of the body – he who has truly acquired the esoterical knowledge of Do-in and of its practice defeats all illnesses before they start.

If only a small percentage of the readers succeeds in breaking through to the esoterical meaning, by studying the metaphysical import of the text rather than by only mimicking the photographs, then Do-in will truly set them in harmony with the movement of the Universe and with the Universe itself.

This is the supreme function of Do-in

Celtic teachings

The Celts played a most important role in the development of Europe. The first civilization of France, the Celtic tradition, is often cited as the fundamental formative agent of France's genial talents. The Celts are often considered as the link between today's civilization and that brilliant one descended from the Antes (Atlantis), the Ge-antes.

The Teaching of Giants

Until they antagonized the gods, the Giants governed the world. Before leaving, they left behind signs in stones, called letters which served as instructions to the Celtic Druids, who, through these, were able to recover and preserve the primitive knowledge, the Voice of Nature.

A certain potion, prepared in the Grail, could cure, rejuvenate or bring back to life. This was the universal medicine of the "Philosopher's Stone". A dream? A fairy tale? But the tradition goes on to say that this same Philosopher's Stone is capable, by acting on the plants, to create mutations. Our seven cereal grains, coming to us from such a distant past that we feel they were created by gods or Giants, were a product of plant mutation. The rose, in all of its perfection, appears suddenly in Persia between the 10th and 11th Century. Before that, the rose was unknown and the closest flower in looks was the hawthorn or the wild dog rose. Thus it appears that it was the Science of Nature that the Giants taught through their "Sounding Stones".

The Giants as Acupuncturists . . .

Agriculture demands a very specific knowledge of earth and agronomic principles. There are definite signs linking the megaliths to the ancient Science of agriculture: Wheat stalk engravings on the large stone pillar of Locmariaquer dolmen and the image of a plow appearing under the "table" of same. If we owe our culture (Agri- and others) to a pre-historic "teaching Civilization", it appears that our mentors had a way of fecundating the earth, using huge stone needles we now call megaliths or dolmens.

Since ancient times, these stone needles have been considered as "Fertilizing Stones" and often times described as "Defense against water". Earth is living matter, possessing an orderly web of energetic current ley lines. These stone needles, still implanted along the earth's meridians are a form of acupuncture of the globe. Our titanic masters possessed an uncanny knowledge of the earth, its formation and its life forces. They dwelt in specific areas, not only for their agricultural possibilities, but also because they found them favorable to the psychic perfecting of man. A study of the geographical location of these spots, reveals that all these lie on a spiral; as if earth, in its formative stage, jelled upon a spirallic system. In the center of each of these regions, remains of megalithic monuments are found as well as definite behaviour patterns still discerned in the local population of today.

For instance: These age-old earth pulsations today still create areas of:

Land of possessed souls
in and around Louviers (France)

Land of sorcery and alchemy
in and around Lyon

Land of miracles and seers
in and around Lourdes

plus many focii of "healers", "poets", "sorcerers" and "artists" elsewhere.

When the earth influence and pulsation becomes too strong, some regions become areas of "hysterical manifestations", unfit for human habitat.

Not only did these lapidary signs, these "letters" serve as instructions from the Giants to the Druids, but ancient tradition, dating from before the Gauls, knew them to be amplifiers of the earth's energy: The "Sounding Stones" that are the dolmens.

". . . then the sons of the God began to notice the daughters of men, that they were good looking; In spite of their purity, the desire was born in the angels of heaven to unite with these attractive creatures . . . when the sons of the God continued to have relations with the daughters of men and they bore sons to them, they were the mighty ones who were of old, the men of fame. They numbered two hundred who descended upon the mount of Hanon."

First Book of Enoch
Chapter VI Genesi

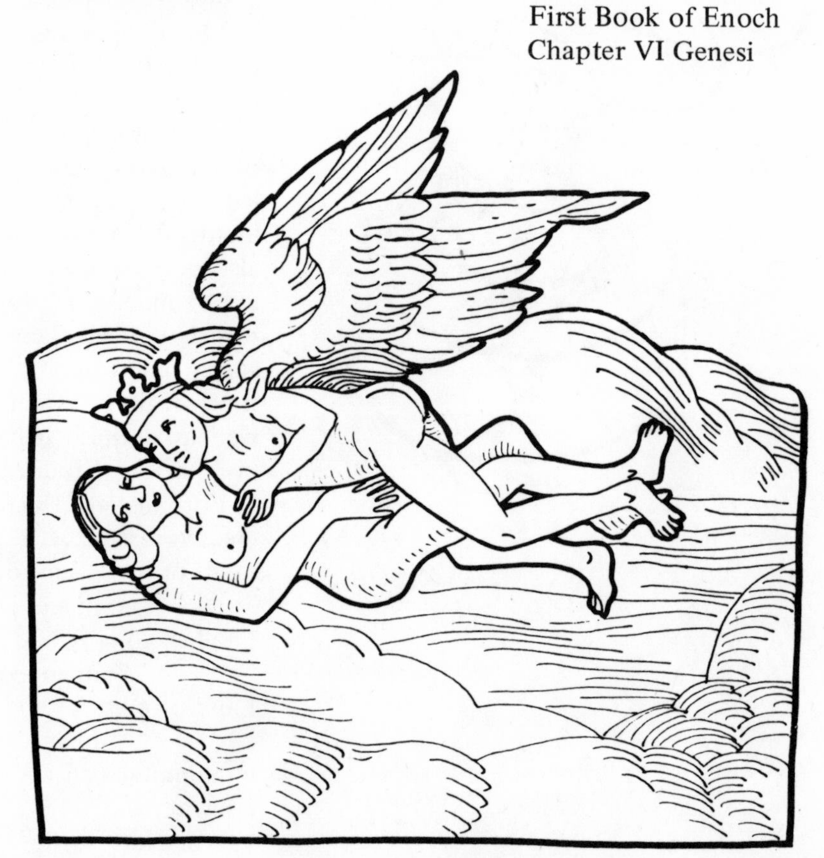

The above quote informs us that the quality of man was regenerated by the fecundating of his daughters by the sons of God. It would appear that the "Teaching Civilization" left its mark on the soil and the fertility of the earth as well as on its population.

. . . and the Gothic Cathedrals as textbooks.

The concept that European gothic cathedrals are metaphysical textbooks is no longer a theory. Openly displayed in the rose of the stained glass window, the glyphs and the gargoyles are the signs offering mankind specific instructions for the utilization of cosmic energy.

The missing Word is there, engraved in stone and fused in glass. In Fulcanelli's Le Mystère des Cathédrales, much of the Word is made intelligible as a technique for mankind's own evolution and spiritual development. Fulcanelli's entire work is concerned with lucid interpretation of the hieroglyphs in the cathedrals of Europe.

One of the mysteries of the cathedrals is the making of the Elixir, the Philosopher's Stone, often thought to be the mysterious fountain for the transmutation of gold as described in details in the bas-reliefs and the figures of stone. Yet, throughout their monumental textbooks, the master builders offer even more precious substances: Truth, reality, the Voice of Nature and "With Light, Salvation".

Through an eastern window . . .
A Pattern for Do-in on the cathedral floor

In the dolmens, the cromlechs as well as the carvings of the floors of cathedrals, a webwork or a labyrinth is inscribed. Some feature an inner chamber, others a stone platform, sometimes a curved gold bar inlay represents the sun rising over the east. The initiates danced along the carved patterns. According to the signs, they pointed their body in turn to the different sources of planetary and telluric currents, allowing their loins and their solar plexuses to be permeated with cosmic energy. To primitive people such as the Druids and the initiates of the secret guilds, the planets and the earth cycles with-held few secrets.

The mazes, patterns and labyrinths are carved records of the laws of the Cosmos, but they are also textbooks written in the stone and held within the metaphysical influential areas of the dolmens and gothic edifices. In essence, the teachings are about man and his dependency upon the Voice of Nature.

Modern Clinical Do-in in China...

The traditional Chinese therapists working in today's hospitals trace the origin of their particular form of Do-in therapy used for the cure of many diseases, to the early practices of monks and genies who used the techniques of *Tao-Yinn* (Do-in) and the *Circulation of the Breath* for: *Making the Body clean and light.* Thus, the ancient sages knew that the practice of Do-in possessed therapeutic and curative powers.

Breathing exercises form an important part of the Yoga practice in India. These Buddhistic teachings were brought into China around the first century of the Christian era but the book: *The Yellow Emperor Classic of Internal Medicine* and the expert opinion of Oriental scholars prove to us that therapeutic breathing and Do-in (*Tao-Yinn*) exercises existed seven centuries before the introduction of Yoga on the mainland of China.

When Buddhism and Yoga began influencing China strongly, the practical healing aspects of Do-in were lost and only the religious implications such as *Become like Buddha, Calm the Spirit* and *Make the Heart Pure* became the primary aims of what was once a self-healing art unifying the physical body with the cosmic forces.

China always loved physical culture, games and dances. The early form of physical culture was Tao-Yinn or induction breathing exercises.

Our definition of Induction breathing massage is "A massage which produces a reaction of energy flow in a related part of the body without actually contacting that part".

The method showed two complementary aspects:
One based on **No-move** *(Ch'i chung)* and the other based on **Movement** *(t'ai-chi-ch'iuan)*

No Move In the first, No-move, the breathing action is directed or suspended so as to shut in and mix the breath *(Ki)* with the body fluids, waste matter and excesses. Or, by concentration of thought, the breath is conducted to the parts of the body in need of special cleansing care along with self-massage of the inductive (related) parts. It is in this way that fatigue and cyclic fevers are treated according to the *Nei-ching.* The same method is used for prolonging life.

Movement The other style of gymnastics, named after the Tai-ch'i symbol, also engendered and perfected life through maintenance of beneficial flow of breath, blood and *Ki* within the body. Following the symbolic form of the circle, all moves of this gymnastic issued from the body center of gravity (Hara). The movements were circular and spread throughout the whole body. All of these motions were so continuous, like the flow of a river, that they received the name of *Long Boxing.*

For the new initiate or the patient who needs regeneration, the actual Do-in exercises are preceeded by a week of *Ch'i-chung*, fast and prayer to set the imagination at rest and to expel wandering thoughts and noxious body wastes. Then begins the directing of the breath in the three areas of the Triple Warmer. When the breathing is even and the movements round, long and relaxed, the will readily achieves Fullness and Emptiness of any part on demand. The general feeling of ease spreads throughout the natural body with supple and controlled muscles and viscera, limbered cerebral-nervous (backbone) meridian, relaxing of the sexual organs and of the cortex, easing of the shoulders and free flexing of the seven articulations of the arm. The sublimation of the mind automatically follows.

It was *Bodhiharma* who brought the principle of Do-in into China in 530 B.C., to enable his monks to maintain their body in the Tao. This series of ten exercises *(i-chin-chung)* prescribed certain body attitudes *(Asanas)* and the control of breath and sensory motors.

The monastery of *Shao-lin* in Hanan was the place where the father abbot further refined the boxing technique to 18 basic movements (now named afther this abbey).

Under the Sui-dynasty, the inductive methou Do-in-fa *(Tao-yinn-fa)* developed further and practicing students used the breathing exercises known as *(Yun-hing-ch'i)* to remain awake throughout the night while sitting in the seiza posture, to arrest their heart beat or breathing at will and start it again and

to remain unharmed by blows or sustain burns without pain or injury.

The advent of Buddhism in China saw the acceptance and widespread usage of Tao-yinn by doctors, boxers, Confucians, Taoists as well as Buddhists. Northern China developed its own style which became based more on muscular strength and an exteriorized form of boxing *(shao-lin)*. The South concentrated on the internal fortitude development with emphasis on yielding, flexibility and the technique of evasion; obliging the adversary to exert himself futilely in attacks until he was placed in an unfavorable position and retreated. To develop fortitude against an illness, the Southern Chinese concerned himself with the internal parts of the body *(nei-chung)* which involved not only healing by breath but also some twisting (wringing out) and crouching positions *(seiza, etc . . .)* for forceful expelling of the illness.

Inner and outer unions

Further, this fortification and healing method also consisted in unifying the physical attributes and the physical areas. With *Shen-ning*, the initiate was taught to unify the inner and outer functions and parts of his body in the following order:

The three inner unions:
1. Emotions united to the wisdom
2. Wisdom united to the breath
3. The breath united to the strength

The three outer unions:
1. The shoulders united to the rib cage
2. The elbows united to the knees
3. The hands united to the feet

Kung-fu and Do-in

In 1779, a missionary, Father Amiot, was able to describe very minutely the defense discipline of the Southern Chinese which was named Kung-fu. In 1881, over a centry after Father Amiot's work, a very complete compilation of illustrated Do-in gymnastics of China appeared under the title of *Nei-chung-t'su-shuo* by the author: *Wang-Tsu-yuan* who died in 1897.

In the last 13 years, healing with these breathing exercises has been aptly renamed "Medical Gymnastics" and has been further refined in Russian clinics along with thalassotherapy, heliotherapy, lunotherapy and self-massage. This incorporation of ancient healing arts in a modern country has been noted by Dr. G.I. Krasnoselsky (Moscow 1961).

In 1968, there were no less than seventy therapeutic clinics in the People's Republic of China using the above described treatment methods specifically for curing: Ulcers and gastric ptosis, chronic constipation, dyspepsia, tuberculosis, hypertension, neurasthenia, etc . . .

Why Do-in therapeutics work in China and Russia . . .

The Unique Principle underlying all of the traditional oriental medicine is fundamental to the understanding of why it works so well in the East. The effectiveness of this ancient medicine is undeniable (and proven by forty centuries of practice) but the Oriental patients are an entirely "Different Breed" from their Western counterpart.

When an Oriental man becomes a patient, intuitively he knows that his own misguided deeds brought him to the illness stage. He does not expect a miracle cure but rather seeks from his advisor superior/physician a gradual rebuilding of health in which he will be expected to do his share. He is a patient in the true sense of the word and understands that healing depends on the cyclic ebb and flow of his own vital energy.

Today, Western patients, as a rule, demand and still expect from their physicians a fast and somewhat spectacular cure -- (this explains why acupuncture, with its promises of instant cure became such a fad in the U.S.) -- The same Western patients and the modern physicians who cater to them, place their hopes chiefly on pharmaceutical drugs, injections and surgery rather than in a biological and physiological restoration of the body's inner mechanism.

Yin and Yang in Healing

Every facet of the Oriental Traditional medicine is based on the Yin Yang principle. The part of medicine we are concerned with here: Do-in or Tao-yinn also obeys the Unique Principle of antagonistic-complementary forces. The principle of Yin and Yang as well as its applications in medicine has been covered in many writings, so these need not be repeated here.

The Circulation of Ki

The term *Ki* or *Ch'i,* meaning breath, air or life's energy has also been described and defined elsewhere but Ki is such an important concept for the understanding of Do-in that further defining of it is needed.

The vital energy of Ki rules the interaction of Yin and Yang forces in each living being and in the cosmos as well. Ki stimulates the activity of all inner organs and a lack of its circulation or a disturbance of its flow is the basic cause of illness.

Ki, in modern language, is the electromagnetic force that holds living and non-living matter together. When it is present in proper amount, it hold the cells of our body together. When this flow stops, matter no longer holds cohesively and rapidly decomposes.

The Regulation of Ki

Ki is absorbed by our body as we require it. We regain the energy we spend by absorbing external elements such as: Food, oxygen, light, sound, thoughts, vibrations and transforming these into flowing Ki or energy. A living organism depends on whatever can be taken from its environment and assimilated for its Ki. From the definition of Ki above, we see that the main purpose of Do-in therapy exercises is to either produce more, circulate, regulate or calm the Ki energy within the body or, to knowingly seek the proper environment that will supply the most favorable Ki.

A DEFICIENCY OF Ki: Signs of a deficiency are hypotonicity of skin, paralysis, torpidness and sluggishness. (Tonification, supplementing and stimulation are needed).

AN EXCESS OF Ki: Signs of an excess are: Hypertonicity, hypertension, hypersecretion, spasms and pains. In the latter case, calming and soothing exercises to sedate and drain the organism are indicated. Redistribution of Ki to depleted parts of the body is also required.

Proper Ki is required for all body and mind functions, for glandular and organic functions as well as superficial sensory centers of the face and skin and for emotional and nervous response.

Traditional Oriental medicine stresses emphatically that an exercise of the external members only: Arms, legs, trunk and head, without involving "inner activity of organs" is useless and accomplishes no healing action whatsoever. Do-in therapy is not simply "Breathe, work and pause" of arms, legs, head and abdomen but a far-reaching technique which requires the involvement of the entire autonomic nervous system, lymph gland network and spiritual consciousness.

Two recent works on Do-in therapy and its effectiveness, validated in scientific clinical studies, show that practicing Tao-yinn breathing sets up new conditional reflexes and "vestigial reflexes" causing hypotension, an inhibition of the cortex with a resulting hyperstimulation of the subcortex and the entire autonomic nervous system.* (The Practice of the Ch'i-chung, by Liou Kuei-chen). Further, Li Fan-ts'ing in 1958 cites the following biochemical changes after the practice of *Nei-yang:*

	Before	After
Hgb	15 grams	16 grams
RBC	4,980,000	5,030,000
WBC	6,700 (Normal: 72% Low: 27%)	7,250 (Normal: 60% Low: 32%)

The author also noted that appetite, weight and urine increased after practice.

In the light of our new understanding of biochemical changes by the yin and yang interaction, we say that Do-in stimulates the circulation of Ki for inner activity yin-passive and for the outer fortifying Yang-active. Ideally, both functions are achieved together by each Do-in breathing exercise, thereby arriving at the "Preservation of life" *(Yang-sheng).*

In the hands of the superior Oriental physician, Do-in is a tool which helps the patient overcome his illness; in actuality, the patient heals himself. Since Do-in therapy combines the two antagonists:

Motion and Rest (Discharge)

the first task of the skilled physician is to teach his patient to relax between each movement.

Restless Exercising - No Cure . . .

As a rule, patients know much more about exercises than they know about relaxing. This state of affairs is duplicated in most Western people who usually excel at hard physical calisthenics, jogging, etc . . . But have very little knack for resting rhythmically and reconstructing between exertions. The two cycles: Motion and rest -- need to be performed in the proper rhythmic sequence but the movement must be stopped altogether when it is felt that the inner organs require the regenerative pause (discharge of toxins); The biological demand of the "Discharge Pause" is a "Call of Nature" and it is the heeding of this call which must be learned by the patient.

*Modern physiology approves of the state of *Repose* and calls it "Special protective inhibition of the cerebral cortex". It is further interesting to note that the cortex has been described as the "Gland of Combat".

Active Pleasure

The septal region of the brain – also called "The Pleasure Center" – receives a stimulus at the very onset of any physical activity. Once aroused, this septal region compellingly shakes the patient out of any inherent lethargy. While this awakening in itself is beneficial to the overall condition of well-being of the subject, the danger here lies in the fact that most people feel they know everything and can do all of the exercises unreservedly.

Listen to the Voice of Nature

This eagerness of the patient must be curbed by the instructor since the "Rest-Discharge Pause" of the exercise is of the utmost importance if healing is to be achieved.

The Voice of Nature is the ultimate governor and regulator of all vital processes. Its requirements and demands must be "felt" and "yielded to" by the patient. Any impatience or restless exercising or straining to achieve success more quickly can wreak untold harm. This rushing will not only jeopardize the cure but could also cause physiological damage.

The importance of closely respecting the two cycles of each breathing Do-in exercise cannot be stressed enough. The two phases of the in-and-out breath cause the diaphragm to move and its displacement massages the inner organs. Many exercises also subject the area between the chest and the pelvis to torsion and twisting so as to wring out waste matter. Thus if the combinations respiratory/internal emptying is carried out correctly, "the internal organs gradually obey the dictates of the will and their functioning can be controlled".

REQUISITES FOR THE PREPARATORY FIRST EXERCISE

Serenity and Unity . . .

The daily practice of therapeutic Do-in begins with a special "Internal Fortifying" exercise. In the correct seiza posture – or supine if the subject is very ill –, the patient begins methodically untensing one muscle after another and allowing himself to become relaxed and composed. The sequence of calming each muscle begins at the apex of the head and progresses down the face, neck, lungs, trunk, shoulders, arms, wrists and hands, then on to stomach, liver, viscera, legs, knees and feet to end at the tip of the toes. All of the internal organs as well are brought into this programmed relaxation.

Inner Fortifying and The Breath

The universally available energy of Ki force is directed by the subject. The will directs it to all parts of the body, again beginning at the apex of the head and on down to the tip of the toes. In all cases of localized malfunctions or diseases, the breath is concentrated for a greater length of time to these specific areas.

For patients with very little physical strength left, only a few mild Do-in exercises are prescribed, yet they are capable of overcoming their weakened condition by the daily performing of some moderate medical gymnastics. The alternating Exercise – breathe out - Rest -- cycle releases tension and expells the illness effectively.

Serenity

In all the clinics of China where Tao-yinn is practiced, rooms with a quiet and relaxed atmosphere are provided since the environment for proper healing is most important. Quietness of the spirit as well as relaxation of the entire physical body must be attained before the start of healing Do-in. It is essential that the patient's spirit be thoroughly at peace; if some tension remains, it is transmitted to the posture and from there to the musculature, preventing the flow of Ki. The word: Composure, (in Chinese *shou*) has a somewhat religious meaning today, but it is used and repeated at each exhalation to quieten both spirit and body while sitting in the Seiza posture.

The Seiza posture itself, when executed well, will assure complete rest of the entire physical system, both skeletal and muscular. A deeper view of the Seiza configuration indicates that the flow of Ki energy is measurably enhanced by the junction of the toes to the base of the spine thus recirculating the Ki flow.

Unity

After a few sessions of patient, unhurried coaching by the superior physician, the interplay of the active exercise and the resting period will reveal itself automatically or organically to the patient who is then well on his way to self-cure.

When the subject begins to know the proper rhythm of alternating activity and breathing pause, when he learns to halt the exercise according to the demands of his organism, he has achieved the great step toward regaining his own health. To the Western man, the traditional chinese doctor explains that when one halts the active part of the exercise in order to rest and exhale, the illness leaves the body.

Relaxation – The Missing Link In The West

Relaxation has become somewhat of a misleading word in the western civilization. In order to realize to what point its true meaning has been lost; the healing value of traditional oriental relaxation for the purpose of healing can only be appreciated by one who has actually been taught the preceeding exercise by a superior physician and has practiced it for a certain period of time regularly.

Practical Hints For The Western Man

My own observation among beginners of Do-in practice in so-called "good health" is that, invariably, whether of European or North American origin; they have completely lost the ability to relax and the first "inner fortifying" exercise even when practiced by healthy subjects, may require up to half an hour of calm practice to achieve the desired results.

Drawing from the above comment, it appears that the first condition of regaining health is to achieve proper composure and rest. This first hurdle is a crucial one and necessitates gentle, knowledgeable coaching as well as close attention to the following influential factors:

Natural Environment

Seek contact witn the earth, its elements and its products in purest form: water, salt and air.

Live in a building least impeded by reinforced concrete walls, pipe "iron cages" and plastic substances.

Live and work in natural light, not behind glass (window or sun shades, sun glasses) or under artificial lighting, incandescent or (worse) fluorescent.

Beware of the imbalance caused by positive or negative ion generators.

Avoid proximity of high tension wires or AC conduits.

Wear vegetable-quality clothing and accessories, especially undergarments, select furniture made of natural materials.

Earth magnetic current influence: Quality of life and state of euphoria varies with ley lines and power points of earth.

Astrobiological Effects

Observance of daily, monthly and seasonal cycles. Variation of Ki flow and resistance to diseases change according to cosmic cycles.

Partaking of Pure Food and Water

Vegetal quality food in natural state (unrefined, unchemicalized, fresh, unpreserved and non-sterilized).

Grown in compatible temperature zones.

Judicially cooked and prepared without additives, spices and heighteners (flavors and colors).

Consumed while in prime condition of Ki energy.

Solids chewed and liquids properly mixed with saliva. Ki of water is absorbed in the mouth.

Discharge is Life

In Do-in nothing happens until you breathe out and discharge poisons.

The intake of food is "pre-life" and "Discharge of waste is Life", this has not been said often enough or emphatically enough. Both the physical and the spiritual body require a certain quantity of food in order to maintain the life process but when wastes issuing from the ingested food and from the thoughts assimilated are not discharged or expelled regularly and in the quantity equal to intake, life stops.

Control the Quantity

Nutritional biochemists have studied the link between amount of food intake and lifespan. When the amount of food consumption is halved, beginning in infancy, the lifespan is easily doubled. To maintain or restore the natural balance in adults or children, some control of the quantity ingested will be beneficial but, just as vital, is proper attention to the regular and complete voiding of colon, bladder and all other discharge channels.

Of all mammals, man, and possibly the great apes, receive no stimulation in the perineal, genital or anal region at the beginning of life. Yet all four-footed mammals use licking in these areas which is much more profound in purpose than just washing. This cutaneous stimulation is not only essential for the proper organic and behavioral unfolding of the body but this stimulation insures proper eliminating functions of the gastro-intestinal and genito-urinary systems. Coupled with the forced inactivity, characteristic of the newborn human infant, this absence of cutaneous stimulation by the mother at the onset of life, fails to promote a thorough voiding of the colon and the bladder. The results, plainly visible in early childhood: Balloon-like belly, open-mouthed-breathing (a sign of clogged stomach, bladder and intestines plus laboring lungs), chronic indigestion, skin rashes, etc . . . afflict humans for the rest of their lives.

Diagnostic Self-massage

Pain, experienced when finger pressure is applied to the abdominal area, is almost universal in modern man and denotes a dire need for restorative healing of the entire area between the lower rib cage and the pelvic region. Further, the additional burden of an overloaded and expanded viscera soon creates prolapse. This places undue pressure on the genital and reproductive organs, especially in women, whose sexual parts are internal. After a limited external expansion which relieves pressure, chronic gynecological disturbances set in. It is a sad fact that Hysterectomy, now routinely performed on young women is avoidable merely by decreasing the colon size and burden. Too frequent bladder and colon nature calls are signs of weakened peristaltic muscles and autonomic nervous system and also point to a general loss of body vitality.

When discharge of colon and of bladder are achieved all at once and completely, once in 24 hours for the colon and no more than three times for the bladder, this is a sign of strong and functional eliminating organs. If the frequency for anyone is twice or three times the above figures, the organism is headed for trouble and restorative Do-in for these particular functions is strongly indicated. Since most Western men and women of today have been raised without the benefit of tactile stimulation of the perineal region, several of the Do-in exercises are specifically designed to restore intuitive, autonomic and energetic discharge of toxins.

The Skin and Discharge

Traditional Oriental medicine views the entire skin surface as an organ. Its porosity allows not only breathing in of Ki, air, light and cosmic vibrations but also permits rapid elimination of surplus matter and fluids. As an elimination organ, it is ready to take over the functions of the kidneys when these fail or become overburdened. The skin becomes a backup system with a generous capacity. But even with its vast resources (18 square feet of body surface -- two million sweat glands) it sometimes finds itself unable to cope with the excessive amounts of urea from animal meat and fats, synthetic substances such as food additives, sugar, drugs, sweeteners, artificial coloring and flavoring agents as well as all antibiotics.

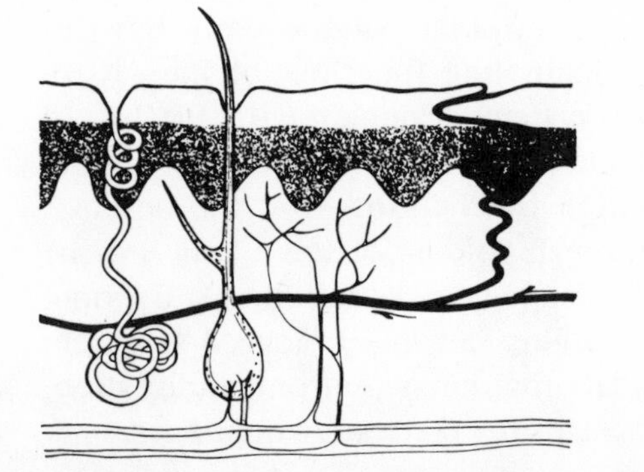

This "Inability" to sweat

The sweat gland is buried one-fifth of an inch below the skin and each one has a spirallic duct tightly coiled, rising to the surface (6 miles of ducts). An average cool day will see the ducts of a healthy man expel at least a half pint of moisture, salts and body waste without any outward signs or awareness of perspiration by the subject. Hard physical work on a hot day wring out up to 7 quarts of toxic moisture. In the case of most diseases, even mild, these 6 miles of ducts become tense, clogged and inoperative due to autonomic muscle spasms.

Heat and steam baths actually inhibit the flow of perspiration through the duct mechanism. Daily hot showers and baths do to a lesser degree. Cold water body rub,–the ablutions of Do-in,– while actually painful to the spasm-riddled skin of most, will restore the autonomic duct function.

The coiled ducts of the sweat glands are regulated by the autonomic nervous system under the direction of the Triple Warmer diffuse organ. The Triple Warmer has ceased to function well (since man surrounded himself with artificial heating and cooling) to such an extent, that the Triple Warmer is no longer acknowledged by modern biology. This breakdown prevents the skin from performing its backup function, closing the only emergency pressure valve available to the ailing kidneys. This is why all skin diseases can be traced originally to kidney malfunction. The major causes of blockage are:

1. Excessive consumption of ANIMAL PROTEIN
2. Consumption of REFINED SUGAR
3. All other YIN factors: Fruits, juices, chemicals, drugs.

The first and last causes are hardest to cure.

The Hair

The glands of the skin manufacture a lubricant which is used primarily for waterproofing body hair. Primitive man's hair also gave him protection from heat and cold. The insulating properties of the hair covering is greatly increased when the hair is made to stand up. When a chill comes, the cold receptors in the skin inform the brain; shivers and gooseflesh pebble the skin as the hair muscles make the hair stand erect thus giving greater warmth for fighting off cold. At the same time, the Triple Warmer meridian begins to stimulate the three warmer organs, shuts down the blood surface vessels thus increasing the amount of energy flow to the skin. The blood supply bypasses the skin in order to remain inside and protect the vital internal organs.

The skin becomes pale from lack of blood and continues to shiver and increase its mechanical activity. Fear will create an identical reaction: Pale skin and increase of internal blood supply

Stimulated by heat or by hard physical activity, the blood vessels dilate, the skin reddens and becomes flushed as the Triple Warmer begins radiating heat to the outside in order to dissipate it. Anger and aggressiveness will trigger the same reaction, especially in the two meridians of Brain-nerve governor and Conception vessel, both ending at the face which will become flushed and the hair of the neck will be erect for the duration of the emergency.

The condition of the body hair along with that of the skin is ruled by the lungs. Healthy hair denotes good lung function. Women possess the same number of follicles but their hair is much finer than men's and almost invisible. Split hair and bushy hair show, not only poor lung function, but also malfunction of sexual organs.

Do-in massage stimulating the Lung and Circulation-sex meridians will correct baldness.

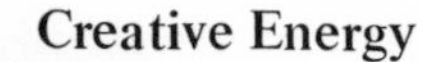

Creative Energy

Creative energy could not exist without the two antagonistic forces. The ancients called these the two forces of Yin and Yang and conceived the world as being in a constant state of change due to the expansion of one causing the contraction of the other.

In our time, the scientific laws of conservation of energy, those of electromagnetic polarity, as well as the systole-diastole of our heart are examples of this principle.

Granted that the forces of Yin and Yang are complementary – but to regard the Creation only in the form of these two opposites could lead to Manichaenism -- so the Chinese always represent these forces with their Pa-Koua which represents the various elements and the three circles.

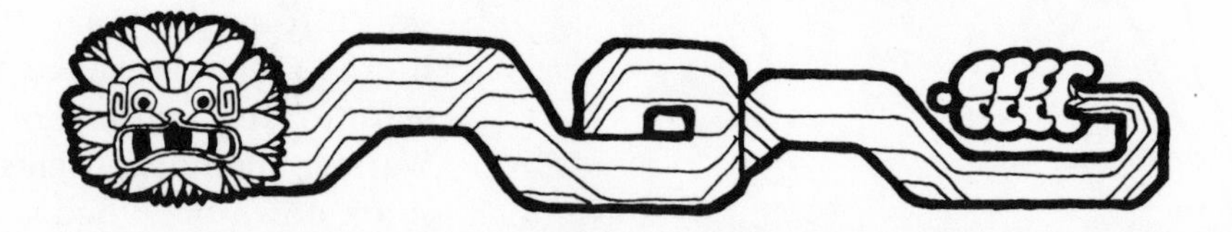

> Energy will do anything that can be done in the world; and no talent, no circumstances, no opportunities will make a two legged animal a man without it.
>
> Goethe

Energy The Primitive Concept

In the mind of the traditional superior physician, the energy is always considered as a "Potential, ready to do work". The quality of being alive comes from the transmutation by the body of: Air, water, light, minerals, food, cosmic vibrations, knowledge and love into energy.

In the universe, this principle of transformation of energy is constantly at work. Because of their complex structure, human beings can be considered the most efficient of all known forms of energy transformers.

The conversion of energy within man is made from many sources, we classify these into various categories to render their study easier but not much will happen until these different energies are duly absorbed by our organism for proper utilization, and that ability depends primarily upon the nature and the condition of our organism.

Once absorbed, the energy demands unimpeded free circulation to maintain continued good health. This can only be accomplished when the organism is free of accumulated toxins and debris. Optimum flow of energy requires periodic and complete discharge of these toxins.*

At this point, an understanding of the concept of circulatory energy within our body is important; part of the diagram – first presented in the chapter "Biocosmology and Do-in", is reproduced here for clarification of the concept.

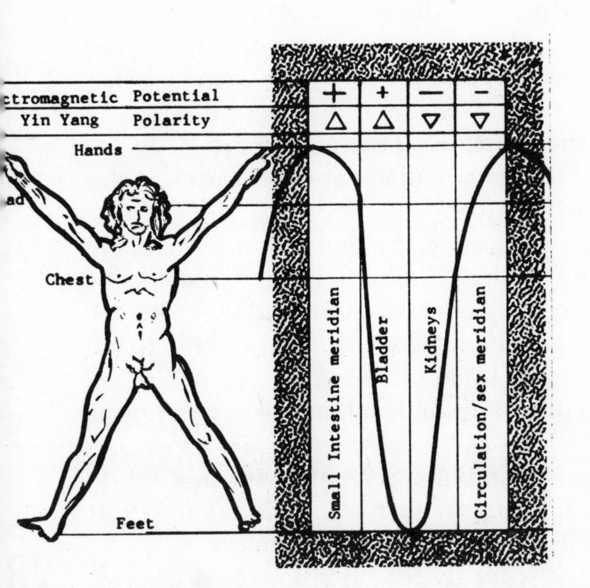

Traditional medicine considers that the energy flows within channels called meridians. In the course of the circulation through the various successive meridians, the polarity (yin-yang) of the energy changes with each passage from downward to upward direction. Thus, on the opposite page, we have shown where the reversing of directions occurs. When meridians are designated as Yin or Yang, this distinction does not mean antagonistic to each other – working against each other –, rather the energy is qualified:
Yang meridian – energy possessing a dynamic quality (active)
Yin meridian – endowed with inertia polarity (receptive)

* See the Chapter: "Discharge is Life".

Inductive Massage

Induction Massage. **A massage which produces a reaction of energy flow in a related part of the body without actually contacting it.**

Depending on their mode of, and the strength of the action, this form of massage will either **Tonify**; by light, soft, superficial and rapid strokes which will strengthen the energy of one organ . . . or **calm**; by slow, deep and sustained pressure which will disperse and redistribute the stalled energy, allowing the entire organism to benefit from the surplus. -- In the end result, **calming** is the greater stimulation.

There are seven manners of application:

1. Rubbing and friction (of varying pressure).
2. Deep pressure with the ball of fingers or fingernail dug into the skin (at the exact acupoint.)
3. Percussion: Light fingertip drumming, finger pad tapping, finger or hand slap up to clenched fists (small hammer).
4. Twist and Torsion: Twisting of the body (or part of it) by two equal opposite forces - also pinching and twisting.
5. Pulling and pushing: Pulling the skin taut and pushing to wrinkle. (alternatively in a straight line along the meridian, making certain that the adjacent meridian is not touched.) Also stretch and compress - hand squeeze, kneading and pulling of the involved muscle and milking between fingers and toes.
6. Scraping and raking: Scraping with nail (s) on skin surface, raking with hooked fingers into soft tissues, or fingertips digging and pulling.
7. Shaking off (mostly for expulsion) to discharge: Hands, arms, legs, feet, head or entire body.

...about Ear Acupuncture and Foot Reflexology

Certain body zones are often considered as being particularly receptive to either massage, acupuncture or inductive healing treatment. These techniques which are restricted to localized areas are helpful but tend to become fragmentary and soon exclude or disregard the fact that the body should be viewed as a whole.

These specific areas of the body receive more concentrated attention because, as a rule, they are overlooked and therefore under-stimulated.

The ears, which are an extension and a reflection of all of the body's organs and their condition, have rapidly become atrophied and shriveled in recent generations. The configuration of the earlobe, for instance, gives an accurate report on the individual's potential for happiness, biological strength and fortune. These dispositions and qualities are exhibited in fleshy, long and pendant (hanging) earlobes, well-separated from the cheek. All great men and philosophers including very successful men in a material sense such as millionaires and tycoons exhibit these earlobes. Many people today, even the frantic breed of tycoons, sport stunted, gnarled and creased earlobes tightly welded to the cheek. This betrays a depleted and deficient organism.

The balance of the ear form denotes very accurately the chronic physical and mental conditions of the individual. Local treatment of the ear by acupuncture corrects effectively because of this inductive relationship.

Pulling the ears of a youngster who misbehaves can now be seen as effectively correcting an organic condition, a restoration of function. Vigorous washing behind and around the ears, with lots of cold water can also be viewed as an efficient restorative massage. Several specific ear Do-in massage exercises are given in the practical section but we should always keep in mind that the quality of the Ki flow depends on the condition of the nervous system and on the state of the meridian system. Since both of these are present and accessible in the overall skin area of the entire body, a faster and more thorough regeneration will be achieved if the organism is treated as a whole by Do-in self-massage.

The ear is a complex sense organ endowed with a hundred acupoints. Its accessibility makes it ideally suited for needle as well as finger stimulation. The origin of some of these techniques is lost in ancient oral tradition, others are intuitive and many people today still twist or pull their earlobes when perplexed, spontaneously re-inventing this healing technique.

Taking Your Shoes Off is not Enough . . .

Equally effective is the series of foot exercises and these are given an extensive pictorial demonstration for the benefit of modern man whose feet have become "of clay", brittle and unyielding. The aim in these exercises is to restore the faculty of the feet to their "all terrain" feature.

The Shoe

With its rigid sole, the shoe prevents beneficial walking, massage and automatic acupressure stimulation of the plantar area of the foot. Toes are similarly held rigidly and have often lost their original flexibility.

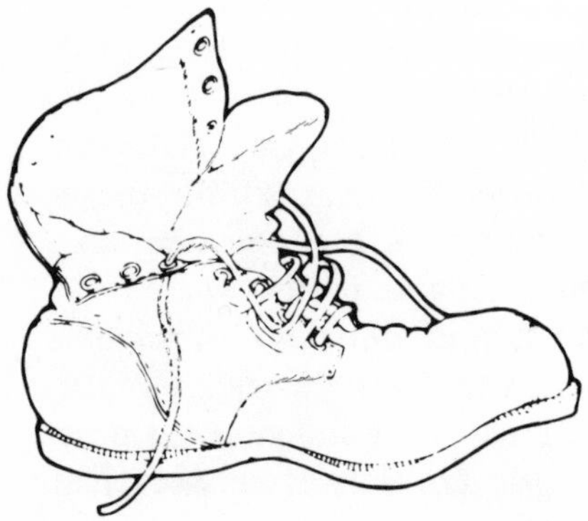

One of the beneficial stimulation for the stiff feet of civilized man is walking barefoot on the stones and twigs of nature's pathway. When this is not readily available induction massage of the foot by stepping in place on an open box full of pebbles is a worthwhile substitute.*

The origin of organic disorders being insufficient discharge of excesses, it is logical and necessary to precede a decongesting foot massage by a thorough whole body massage, otherwise the toxins will remain blocked at the hip or knee levels and will not be expelled. The meridians will properly disperse and redistribute the excess energy of one meridian only when no blockage exists between the digestive cavity and the feet.

Swedish Muscular Massage -- A Child of Do-in

Because it treats certain precise areas of the body, Do-in could be considered to be a massage. But it must be stressed that since it affects only a very minute surface of the skin, therapeutic Inductive Do-in operates on a non-mechanical basis.

We may ask, how could an intervention mechanically so slight, give results superior to the ordinary classical Swedish massage which involves work on the muscles, a muscular group or even the actual deep organ? The fundamental difference between the two techniques:

Swedish deep massage is a **mechanical** action whereas Do-in inductive massage is an **energetic** action.

*A molded "finger" mat is available from: Step One, 558 E. 23rd St., Chico, Ca. 95926.

Do-in self massage originated and validated the principle of meridians and pressure points now employed by the acupuncturists. When this original concept of Energetic action and Ki flow was no longer understood, deep muscle massage came into being and received more impetus as protein coagulation settled in muscular structures due to excessive eating and the trend to more animal protein consumption. This in turn created in the patient a lack of response to simple finger-pressure and hand treatment which led to the necessity of puncturing of the skin by needles and Swedish massage.

Localized Healing Self-massage

When faced with a particularly painful localized pressure point, it is advisable to first apply a light pressure treatment to it for two or three minutes or until the pain subsides. The rapid short strokes will measurably subdue the pain. Shortly afterwards the deep sustained and prolonged fingertip treatment, in the direction of the Ki flow within the underlying meridian can safely be carried out with much less pain being felt.

However, when pain is experienced on a spot which is not a pressure point, there is little benefit in applying the above technique since no energizing effect takes place outside of the pressure points proper. Rather, it is suggested to seek and treat pressure points surrounding the painful spot.

In any event, it is not advisable to treat pressure points located within swollen or inflamed skin or flesh areas. Scar tissues newly formed on a recent wound have obliterated the underlying pressure point or points, yet it is vital to promote the return of the Ki flow through the disrupted area by judicious massage of the points just above and below, up and downstream, on the through-going meridian.

We remember that pain is created chiefly by an excess of stagnant energy, which needs to be channeled elsewhere or drained out of the body and that this is accomplished by deep, slow and sustained pressure on the points affected. In all cases of excessive stagnant energy -- indicated by pain -- it is generally advisable to exert a draining influence on a centrifugal (yin) meridian in order to promote an outward flow toward the fingers or the toes.

Treating the one side of the body affected with paralysis (contributory cause -- insufficiency or absence of energy in the side affected) requires the "Increase of energy" type massage:

Light pressure, rapid strokes of short duration, on the paralyzed side. But treating the opposite side on the identical symmetrical points with the same "tonifying" technique will fill it also with energy in a quantity sufficient to prevent draining it away from the healthy side by loans to the paralyzed side.

The Superior Physician and Fingertip Healing

The Superior enlightened acupuncturist is not only very fluent and practised in the art of fingertip massage* but in many cases will prefer to use it when his patient is a child or a patient who is fearful of the needle. This traditional physician, in his professional wisdom, knows that acupressure is in no way less effective than the needles. Granted that needles are faster and more spectacularly impressive, but the fingertip massage achieves just as good a result, possibly more time consuming in application, but more easily taught to the patient for self-application.

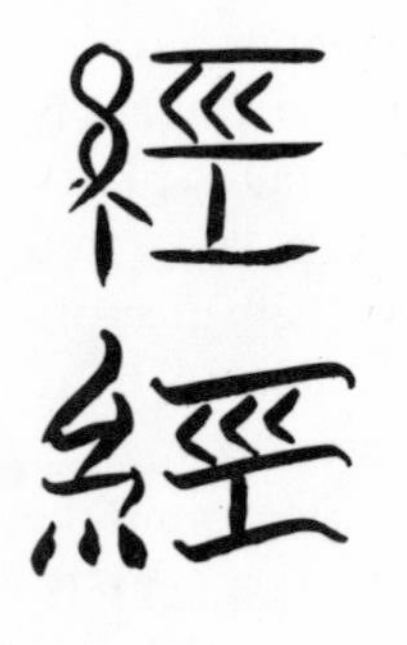

In Ancient China, before the art of writing came into being, Tao-Yinn was taught in the greatest secrecy from parents to children, which kept the art pure and in its most potent strength.

Some time later, but only to teach the sole pupil in private, the ideograms came into being. These were signs traced on the ground and used only to depict the position of relative elements in more graphic terms.

To illustrate this point, we can study the symbolism contained in the concept of "Meridian" in the ancient Chinese ideogram:

For the Do-in student, the above character studied in all of its details yields easily all that is required to understand the universal and total principle of Do-in and Ki, the flow of energy, its structure and meridian.

The left part of the ideogram represents a skein of silk on a staff, the whole meaning a tenuous, threadlike link. The top right part shows running water flowing between two banks which contain it like a flume; a water way. The lower bank merges into a T-square, the universal symbol for work or labour. Thus, we have, thread of silk flow guided by banks (meridians) to channel energy.

What is reproduced above is the most ancient Chinese ideogram and below it is shown its modern counterpart, still legible but requiring a lot more "book" knowledge in order to interpret it.

*"Flat of the nail" (Dialectrical) and fingertip massage have not only proven themselves for the past 5,000 years in China, but have been developed today to the highest degree of precision and effectiveness.

More Secret Teachings

Hermeticism today cloaks much of the essential teachings handed down to Man from his earliest ancestors. The Secret Teachings are closed to man today possibly because if they were widely known, these might be misunderstood and misused.

For my part, I do not believe that receptacles of ancient knowledge: Pyramids, Cathedrals, Stonehenges, have a built-in timing device that will unlock their stores of knowledge when man proves and shows his readiness and receptive state of soul. But I do believe that man will regain his understanding of all cosmic natural forces by gradually returning to paying more and more attention to the Voice of Nature.

In our world today, students of esoterical philosophy are concentrating mostly on Chinese philosophies with much emphasis on Oriental healing arts and medicine. What we refer to as Do-in or Tao-yinn – the regenerative healing exercises designed to regain hearing of the Voice of Nature -- is one of those we classify as Oriental. Yet the knowledge of the series of practices known as Do-in sprang up simultaneously in more than one part of the world. Thus in Europe we find the Keltic race was also recipient and keeper-people of these Hermetic teachings through the ages.

Ki in Kilt

The sound of Ki as in Kilt and Keltic, originated from this group of sages.

Nowadays, the closed teachings of the Kelts or Celts are rediscovered by systematic study at the College of the Druids in Nanterre, France. The lifted sounding stones, the Cromlechs -- similar to the Stonehenge formation across the English channel -- now bear engravings but it is known that the repeated invasions by Runic and Roman "barbarians" are responsible for these carvings. The Druids themselves wrote not on their stones for they had nothing at all similar to writing, theirs was an Earth/Sky Science and it was learned by the student who stood at the proper time-cycle of the day in the sacred stone circles and received the cosmic wisdom in its purest form.

Writing is a Sickness...

Stone Sun Circles and Cromlechs developed out of the need to observe the forces of earth as they reacted to the influence of sky, water and wind forces. The stone formations were truly precise instruments in which the outer physical effects of these elements were shut off so that the Druid initiates could feel and study the metaphysical flow force on his mind and body in a darkened space, shielded from the visible light radiating from the sun and moon. In this manner, with the disciple standing in deep receptive form, he allowed the Ki force to enlighten his wisdom and energize his body with all the strength of the natural forces.

Those were times of no books or clocks. To get information about the right time to sow seeds, there was only the Cosmos itself to read, therefore the initiate watched the action of the sun in and on his stones and read in Nature more vividly than in any book. In the shadow of the stones, the sun spoke straight into him in concrete ideograms and nothing needed to be derived from his intellect.

The ritual of communion with the Voice of Nature began with the daily practice of a form of Do-in at sunrise. All of the initiates observed the breathing-in of the new day and the outcome through their awakened seven senses was not an abstract knowledge but closer to the quickened circulation of the sap or the blood flowing upward within plants and men.

Although this pulsating was strongly physical as each of their plexuses was submitted to the dawning force, the inner stimulation was spiritual as well and enriched their total wisdom.

When the Runic hordes came to the country of Gaul bearing their written tablets, the Druids were shocked and concerned . . . Making notes on matters which could so obviously be read and observed directly in the cosmos made little sense to the Druids. They immediately proceeded to mix special foods and medicine for the poor Runics who suffered from this writing disease and alienation from the Voice of Nature.

Initiations

The Celts received their teachings within the sun circles and the Cromlechs at the proper time-cycle of day, month and year. In contrast, to the daily ritual there were other times when these influences were stronger. What we might call great waves of wisdom as opposed to the lesser daily flow. When great Hermetic secrets had to be revealed, those were the times of season when the initiates, prepared by special regimen followed

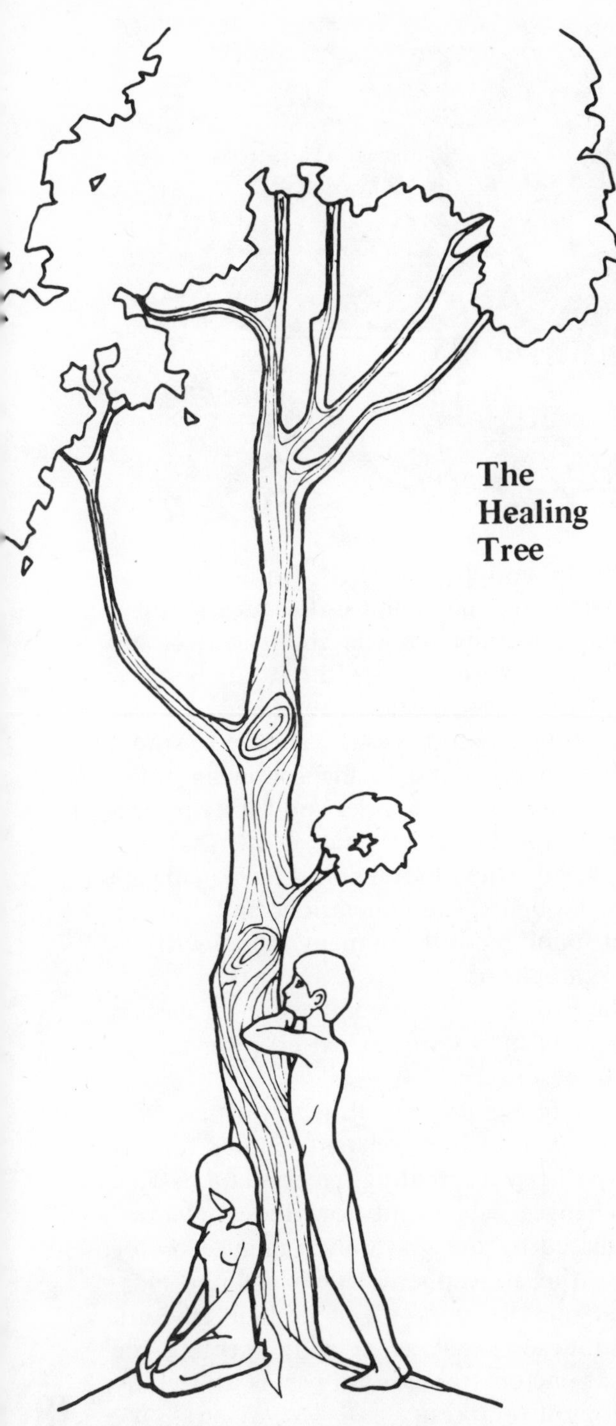

by fasting as well as ablutions, exposed their meridians and the plexuses of their body to the special Nature forces at their strongest peaks. We now call these Equinoxes and Solstices and we speak of these special times as holidays and we may schedule initiations of sorts then, but these seasonal cycles have lost all of their sense/impressions for us. To regain the sensitivity of these rhythms, it takes a complete turnabout, gradually accomplished by leaving the shields of artificial buildings and lights, schedules and living habits.* How far must we go to again instill within us the wisdom of the Voice of Nature? The answer lies in actual practice of natural living and in the closer communion with the earth and its forces.

The Healing Tree

What has remained from the Keltic Earth/Sky science is best exemplified in their Art of Healing and in what has been handed down to us in the form of "Voice of Nature" breathing. The strongest healing of man by a plant is not achieved by drinking a tea made from its leaves or by chewing its berries or stalks. The magnestism of a tree trunk or a stalk and the curative effect of standing in close contact with the shaft of strong plants is being rediscovered and used today.

Two different stances are assumed by the initiate: 1. With the whole backbone touching the bark, this heals the nervous system and appears to be much in favor by those city people who return to the woods once in a while: Their intuition leads them to sit at a foot of a tree and lean their back to its trunk. 2. Standing with the entire chest and abdomen placed in contact with the tree and feet either placed on each side of the roots or a couple of feet away from the base. This contact strengthens the vegetative system: Intake of air, digestion of food and reproductive organs. By coincidence, this is one of the first exercises shown me by Sensei Enomoto and it carried with it the admonition to practice this breathing exercise, not against a wall, but on a post or a tree!

A comparative study of human body meridians and plant physiology will demonstrate the value of body contact with the tree and its force.

Two meridians: Brain-nerve Governor, centered on the backside of man, and Circulation-sex, on his front from the pelvic area to the mouth, are single stem meridians and both have an upward direction of Ki flow.

*See "Factors influencing the Ki" at end of "Chinese Hospitals" Chapter.

Beyond Do-in

Much of the experience and the benefits acquired by the practice of Do-in is for our own need and in the present time. Some of the deeper understanding we gain about control and flow of Ki (universal energy) within and without our body, is acquired for the need of the not-so-distant future and a look ahead at the advantages conferred on those who choose to study, practice and teach Do-in are explored in the following notes.

Before embarking on some of the theories and future projections on the development of the Do-in man, I ask that you kindly keep in mind that while the observations I have made are the product of my own thoughts, the conclusions and "Predictions" are not mine but found recorded in many sacred writings and ancient traditional symbolisms.

1. The sun, whether the product of the combustion of carbon and oxygen or a very efficient hydrogen battery, appears to have inexhaustible energy resources.
2. We consider ourselves fortunate that this powerful engine seems to function at such remarkable constant temperature. If it did not, we would experience alternating freezing and baking. Yet, since everything changes, when and how does it change?
3. Of all the energy radiated by the sun, only a minute vector falls on earth. Further, the atmospheric shield and the man-made smoke and dust mantle cuts off a certain amount.
4. From the total of the sun's energy actually meeting the earth, it is estimated that one one thousandth part is utilized by the plant world through photosynthesis.

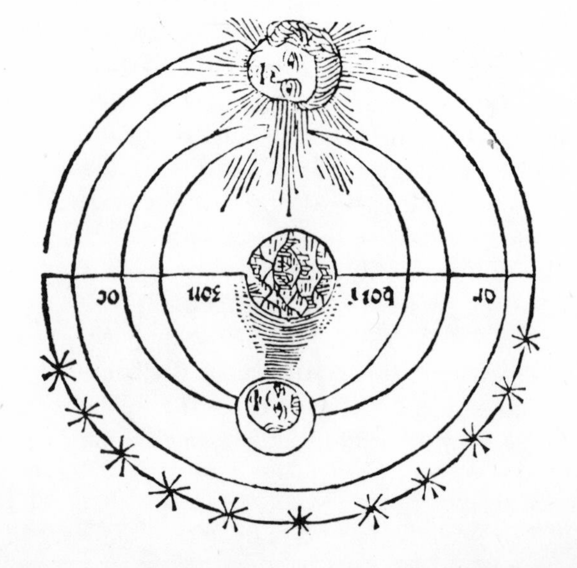

5. When all of the plant life of earth breaks down carbon dioxyde (CO_2) contained in the air to generate organic matter: Starches, glucides, fats and albumins) it fixes 60,000,000,000 tons of carbon per year. While part of this carbon is used by animals, chlorophyll-less plants and bacteria, its return to the atmosphere closes the circle.
6. Another part of the carbon, however, becomes fossil, is stored in the earth and stays out of circulation except for internal combustion.
7. Man also, especially in the last 300 years, is now capable of recovering this stored up carbon and burn it. This consumption of fossil fuels is on a run-away increase.
8. 10,000,000,000 tons of carbon are brought back into the circuit by man every year by petroleum, natural gas, coal, wood and crops burning. The amount of CO_2 present in the atmosphere has been increased by man 40 times since 1900. Man's chemical emissions and firing activity are so strong that they measurably modify the vital balance of the entire earth.
9. If one one thousandth part of the sun's total earth vector is used by plant life – and makes 60,000,000,000 tons of carbon per year -- The part unused for chlorophyllian assimilation is 999 greater or a potential equivalent to 59,940,000,000,000 tons of unused carbon per year, enough to "fuel" man's need for 5,994 years, at present consumption rates!

The Heart of our Universe

1. The ancients believed that the sun, as the heart of our universe, was closely connected with man's heart, the master of body life. Recently, the sun and its disturbances (spots and swellings) has been recognized as having strong influences on human metabolism, specifically on the cardiac and the vascular systems. (Myocardial infarctions always increase in frequency and severity following sunspots activity). It appears that sunspots alter the balance of earth-level ionized magnetic fields which surround us and favorize the formation of blood clots due to the bio-electrical response of our blood plasma.

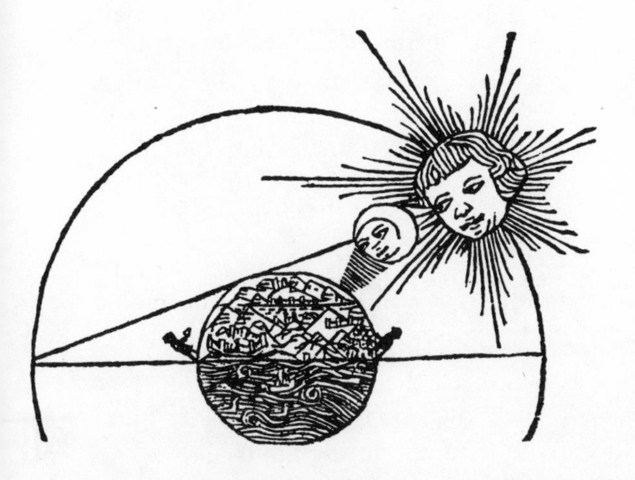

2. For all of the visible occurences taking place on the sun, there are a number of invisible radiations: Increase of U V and X radiations which are followed by Aurora Borealis, magnetic storms, radio interferences plus often an increase of earth rotational speed and measurably shorter days. In the face of these disturbances, Nature in its wisdom, triggers a compensating higher fertility stimulation of all vegetal species to insure their

survival. When solar activity intensifies, earth forces increase in the same magnitude. Recently man has become more aware of the internal energy of his planet, is better able to detect telluric currents by dowsing, has rediscovered ley lines and the kinship of the Ki force of his own body with that of the universe.
3. The same solar electrical forces of storms act directly, not only on the biological but also, on the social and intellectual behaviour of the whole of mankind. Thus the heat and magnetic perturbations of the sun affect the cauldron of knowledge, but also the understanding of man becomes superactive as if to insure his survival.
4. This proliferation in wisdom and in sheer population number is inevitable and just as unavoidable is the multiplication of evil and corrupt beings who appear near the end of a cycle (Plato noted this phenomenon in his writings).

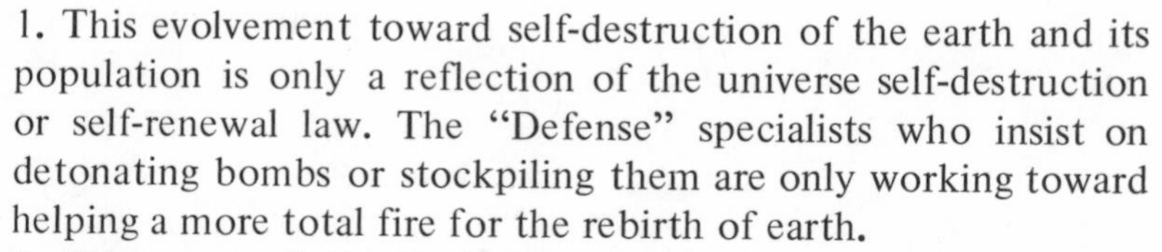

The End of a Cycle

1. This evolvement toward self-destruction of the earth and its population is only a reflection of the universe self-destruction or self-renewal law. The "Defense" specialists who insist on detonating bombs or stockpiling them are only working toward helping a more total fire for the rebirth of earth.
2. Those same "scientists" may not survive the grand cooperation between their puny megathons and the large one inevitably emanating from the sun as a harmonic consonance reaction. They may also get blamed for being the instigators of the holocaust, although their self-destructive tendencies originated in the "heart" of the solar system and only resonated in their human brain. Unconsciously, we all possess this universal self-destructing drive which helps nature to evolve by destruction and subsequent rebirth.
3. The history of our planet repeats itself and is punctuated by cataclysmic renewal cycles. There is little doubt that earth is approaching the end of such a cycle and that mankind on its own volition is fast splitting into two groups.
4. Survivors of a trial by any elements (water, ice, fire, etc . . .) pass from the old world in their bold attempt to plant themselves in the emerging new world. Unerringly led through the change by instinctively listening to the Voice of Nature, they discovered – dowsing with their own body – the few safe spots on earth and the self-discipline required during the trial.

5. When a shipwrecked man is found clinging, barely alive, to flotsam, any tender loving care or pampering is sure to terminate him. The wise rescue crew spits upon him, bullies him and keeps him hungry for some time after his ordeal to strengthen him for his restitution to the normal soft life.

It is difficult to picture the further trials facing the survivors emerging in a world whose sun recently suffered a strong fever and caused a giant upheaval. The sputtering out of the great cosmic heart and its rekindling takes time and requires that man turn inward to Mother Earth for energy, comfort and strength. The initial trial is thus followed by a lengthy endurance period where all of man's intuition is put to the test. The rediscovery of matter created from an infinitely small amount of energy, the conservation of energy and the economical transmutation of energy into heat for the preservation of his body will demand great understanding of the Voice of Nature

The Unvulnerable Man

Pseudo guidelines for the reeducation of the intuitive mind of man using gadgets, machinery and trickery, abound today and have become quite popular. The true guidelines are rarely practiced. The following techniques are closely linked to Do-in and belong in the preparedness training of the enlightened man.

While it is beyond the scope of this Do-in Guide to cover techniques which serve to render man invulnerable in accidents, combats or crises, we mention these special Aikido teachings which are taught today in Hawaii, Japan and the United States by true masters whose techniques are derived from the principle of Do-in.

The interested reader is directed to an illustrated book: "Ki Development Methods, Coordination of Mind and Body" by Master Koichi Tohei.

Kiai

Another valuable teaching, which had almost fallen into oblivion, is found in the secret techniques of instantaneous reanimation called "Kuatsu" and its companion the "Kiai". Used to revive someone in shock, hit by a vehicle or by blows, hemorrhaging or giving all appearances of death, the revival techniques consist of rapid, precise percussions, massages and torsions, similar to those outlined in the "Induction Massage" Chapter of this book but applied with greater strength. In addition, special shouts in major keys producing harmonic sound waves induce excitation of cardiac and breathing functions. Still taught today in secrecy by high ranking Black Belts of Judo, these methods have their origin in China thirty centuries before Christ and were used, in battle, to revive friends and opponents. Today, in Japan, these have been grouped under the name of Kappo.

Linear massage versus Spirallic massage

Close scrutiny of the anatomical structure of a pressure point reveals that a microscopic duct tightly coiled in a spiral, rises from the embedded meridian to the surface of the skin where Ki is absorbed from the ambient environment or its excess dissipated. This structure is what might have led to the relatively recent concept of treating a pressure point by rotating the fingertip with centripetal or centrifugal spirallic motion. The more ancient and more stable concept of linear finger massage, starting just ahead of the pressure point considered -- and ending just a couple of inches beyond but on the line of the meridian in the direction of the flow -- carries much more authority and has a long proven record of effectiveness. This minor controversy is not so important as the necessity of respecting the direction of flow while treating by linear massage.

To understand the importance of this, two examples will suffice:

In the meridian of lungs, the percentage of Yang energy to that of Yin energy varies from 1% at the chest to 50% at the thumb. Our treatment of any part of this meridian will have to conform to the natural tendency of the energy rise. To increase the level of the energy, we will go with the flow, that is toward the thumb in the direction of the increase of Yang. To sedate or diminish the level of energy, we must massage "against the Ki current", that is, toward the shoulders, in the direction of the reduction of Yang.

The three meridians which flow from hand to head: Large Intestine, Small Intestine and the Three Heaters have their proportion of Yang versus Yin varying from 50% at the hand level and reaching 99% at the head. To increase energy on any of their points, a centripetal* – toward the head will be required. To calm or diminish the Yang, a centrifugal movement will be used -- toward the hand.

Stomach, Bladder, Gall Bladder
(All 3) from head -- 99%
to foot – 50% (Yang)
Increased by centripetal --
head
Calmed by centrifugal –
feet

Spleen, Kidneys, Liver
(All 3) from foot -- 50%
to Chest -- 1% (Yang)
Increased by centrifugal –
foot
Calmed by centripetal –
chest

. . . in the direction of the reduction of Yang percentage.

Up stream and down stream

The ball of the fingertip or its nail laid flat begins its pressure action on the acupoint itself and carries the movement one or two inches beyond before lifting the tip of the finger of that hand, the other hand relays the linear movement by acting in turn on the acupoint and underlying meridian, insuring a continuous action by the alternating of the two hands.

Fingers and Toes – The Polarity Changes

The flow of energy is enhanced by Do-in massage and is most easily altered at the finger and toe extremities – the end of the meridian where the polarity changes either from Yang to Yin or from Yin to Yang. Before the meridian ends at the finger or toe tips, a connecting link starts at the wrist or the ankle and internally joins the following meridian. Since the reversing of the polarity takes place within those submeridian links, it is within the areas between wrist and fingers and those between ankle and toes that the alteration and regulation of energy flow can best be made.

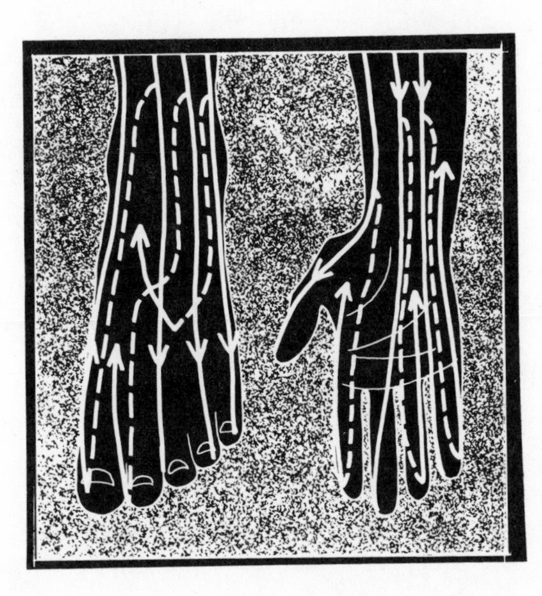

Conservation of energy begins with our body's. Excess of stagnant energy is best utilized to correct a lack of it elsewhere.

The balancing of the flow is practised instinctively by all animals through licking, scratching, stretching and twisting in such a harmonious manner that it treats the whole body; affecting the redistribution of excesses to the deficient areas without technical knowledge or attention to specific symptomatic acupoints.

In the same manner, the most restorative techniques for man, are those Do-in breathing exercises and massages which treat the body as a whole, affecting and harmonizing all of the meridians equally.

The Highest Healer

The highest healer cures by noting and correcting any imbalance in the vital energy flow of a patient. He works with the bipolarity of the Ki:

Yang, the dynamic, the energy of *action*
Yin, the receptive, the energy of *inertia**

To note the condition of the whole person is to locate the "sick Ki", that is, the Ki that has become too receptive when it should be active, or the Ki which turned excessively dynamic when it should have remained inert or receptive.

*The descriptions of deficiencies and excesses mean "Hypo- and Hyper-activity and not emptiness or fullness of Matter within the various organs or their meridians.

The Diagnosis is the Treatment

Finding the Way to Cure is the Diagnosis. The symptoms for any illness vary almost endlessly according to the condition, the age and the life style of each patient; but self-massage treats the whole condition, the body as a whole, positively affecting all of the 12 meridians and their organs.

In the following pages, the signs and the manifestations of illnesses are given for each of the 12 organs along with their functions according to the principle of ancient traditional medicine. We urge the student to apply the "Requirements for optimum performance Suggestions" as well as the daily practice of a broad selection of Do-in breathing exercises. Specific acupoints to be treated for each organ deficiency are also given but these should always be considered as palliative and symptomatic cures. To heal anyone is done by strengthening and harmonizing his Ki. Each person must do this curing by himself; no one else can "cure" him . . . A superior physician can help greatly, pointing out deficiencies in certain functions as well as wrong life style and dietary habits but in the final analysis, the most helpful advice still remains:

"Heal thyself!"

Watergate
its true Meaning

The ruler of a country is wise in the requirements of vital elements for the welfare of the people. Thus, energy sources are not his prime concern since man, earth and sun can always provide adequate energy.

A monarch who spends much time futilely arranging for energy substitutes and distribution systems instead of concentrating on the quality, purity and adequate supply of the precious elements of water, air and salt, is either incompetent or covering up his ignorance. Thus the waterways of the land and the watergates of its inhabitants – kidneys, bladder and gonads – are of prime importance since they alone, insure good supply of the vital elements for earth irrigation and human metabolism. The watergates of the body must also be maintained in excellent condition since water kills fire (inflamation) but too much water (drinking) accumulates in the brain reducing clear thinking and intelligence, leading to tolerance of a bad ruler.

The planting season was heralded by the Emperor, who, in early Spring, went to the countryside with his whole retinue to open the symbolic watergate. One of the first two points of the Lungs meridian *Yun men*, in the language of the scholarly Chinese, means "The gate of clouds," indicating a close connection with water as well as air.

The Do-in man who practices and studies the relative importance of water, air and food elements of his own body, also learns of the functions of the meridians as regulators of these elements. A definition of their role in human metabolism according to the principles of ancient traditional medicine as well as the location and the acupoints to be used for palliative treatment is given in the last twelve chapters of this book.

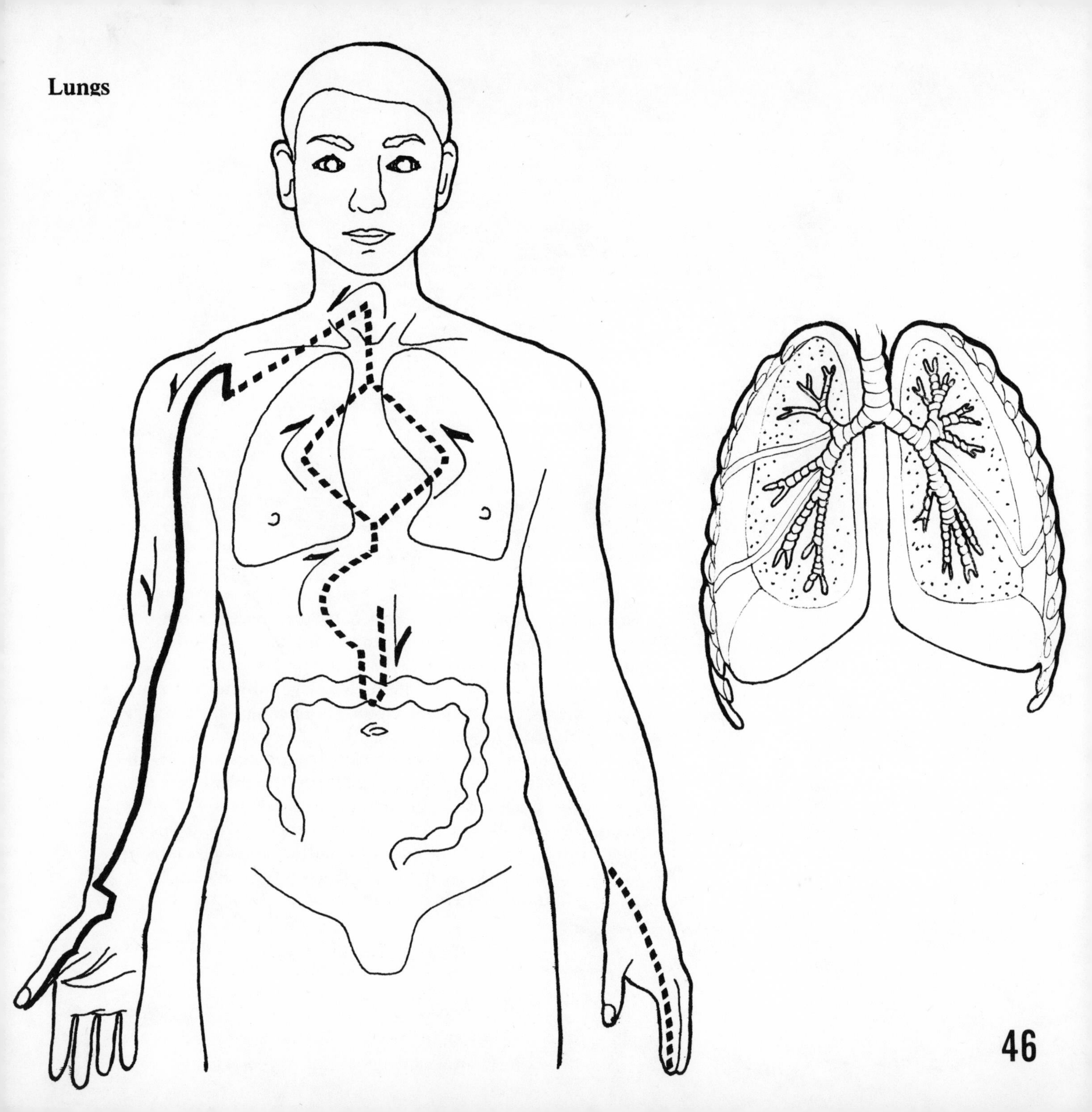
Lungs

Lungs

Tradition

The strength of the entire organism is dependent on the lungs. The first point on its meridian is called "Liberation of Energy" and sometimes "The Gate of Clouds", pointing to the organ's ability to regulate condensation of moisture as well as dry air. Ancient Chinese scholars still use the latter term to designate an aqueduct or a watergate.

The actual course of the meridian begins internally at the solar plexus as a single line which connects downward with the transverse colon then rises while circumventing the stomach. From there it crosses the diaphragm along the lower throat where it splits into two branches. Each of these run through the central upper part of the lungs where the blood supply connects with the lungs. The two separate branches are soon reunited and follow the windpipe upwards until it reaches the gullet. Up to this point, the lung meridian has been internal, deep within the body and responds only to Do-in breathing exercises and inductive (remote) treatment. From this single point in the upper throat, the meridian divides once again and surfaces near the shoulder. Now symmetrical branches rise up to the collarbones and from there go down the front part of the arm to end at the thumbnail. Prior to its ending at the height of the wrists, a connecting branch joins the next meridian of Large Intestine at the index tip. The pressure point located at the wrist is named "maximum whirlpool" indicating, not only the characteristic pulse diagnosis but the focus of energy polarity change.

Function and Value

Lungs supply oxygen in sufficient quantity for proper organic function and combustion and assure the formation of oxyhemoglobin for red blood cells. They also breathe out carbon dioxide gas released by the decomposition of the blood. Other gases are also eliminated in minute quantities: Ether, aromatic esters, turpentine and alcohol.

Requirements for Optimum Function

When an individual possesses good lung function he shows quick and in depth understanding. One who has poor lungs shows melancholy and depression.

Adequate lung ventilation is assured by clean air supply and healthy lung tissues, this is vital to good organic life and thought processes. In affluent countries and times, fat as well as thin people have excesses and the lungs require deeper or faster breathing in order to fully oxygenate blood. During the breathing out, elimination and complete cleansing is not achieved, blood impurities remain internally. The condition of modern city dwellers is further impaired by the action of nitrogen dioxide (from smog and tobacco smoke) which further weaken lung sacs and cause constriction and irritation of the bronchial tubes. It should also be noted that most airborne poisons stick to the oxide of nitrogen particles and are thus absorbed in the throat and lungs. From 1956 until 1974, the percentage of oxides of nitrogen in city air has doubled.

When blood is acid and contain fatty acids it adheres to the lung sacs and makes nicotine and other poisons stick to the sacs in turn, showing that acidosis is the real cause of lung cancer.

Mucous membranes of nose, mouth and pharynx are coated with small blood vessels and serve to warm and humidify or cool and dry the incoming air depending on the ambient temperature. Lungs are thus protected by the upper respiratory tract which prepares the inspired air. Through the mouth breathing bypasses this filtering/conditioning process and indicates over-eating, distended stomach and lack of proper assimilation/elimination of food. The entire respiratory tract is lined with cilia (eyelash-like hairs which are constantly trapping and rejecting undesirable dust, poison particles), even minimal amounts of tobacco smoke and smog are sufficient to paralize this defense mechanism. Prolonged inhalation of nicotine, nitrogen, fluoride and lead causes total destruction of the cilia.

Lung ailments -- Danger signals

The lungs are connected to the condition of the skin and body hair. Therefore when these exhibit a healthy condition, they indicate that the lungs are in excellent condition. Split hairs indicate poor kidney and ovaries. Hiccoughs are a chronic inspiratory reflex of the diaphragm which betrays an attempt by the sympathetic/centripetal and the phrenic nerves to re-establish balance in the lung and kidney functions.

Yawning is an instinctive reaction effective in introducing larger quantities of air into the lungs, indicative of malfunction or slowdown of lungs or poor absorption of oxygen due to toxins, fatigue or lack of energy. All illnesses create a lack of oxygenation. Persons with heart disorders yawn frequently due to poor circulation of blood. Anxiety and boredom are also conducive to yawns and denote primarily a diseased condition of the body in general and of the lungs in particular. To provoke coughing or yawning at will such as in Do-in exercises is most beneficial in relieving underoxygenated lung conditions.

Relief of pain and symptoms

Any acute respiratory ailment . . . . . . treat Lp 1
Chills, bronchitis, low energy,
facial spasms, shock, paralysis . . . . . . treat Lp 7

Throat, pharyngitis, cough,
asthma, gum inflammation . . . . . . treat Lp 11
(calm for 30 seconds)

THE WIND DRAGON.

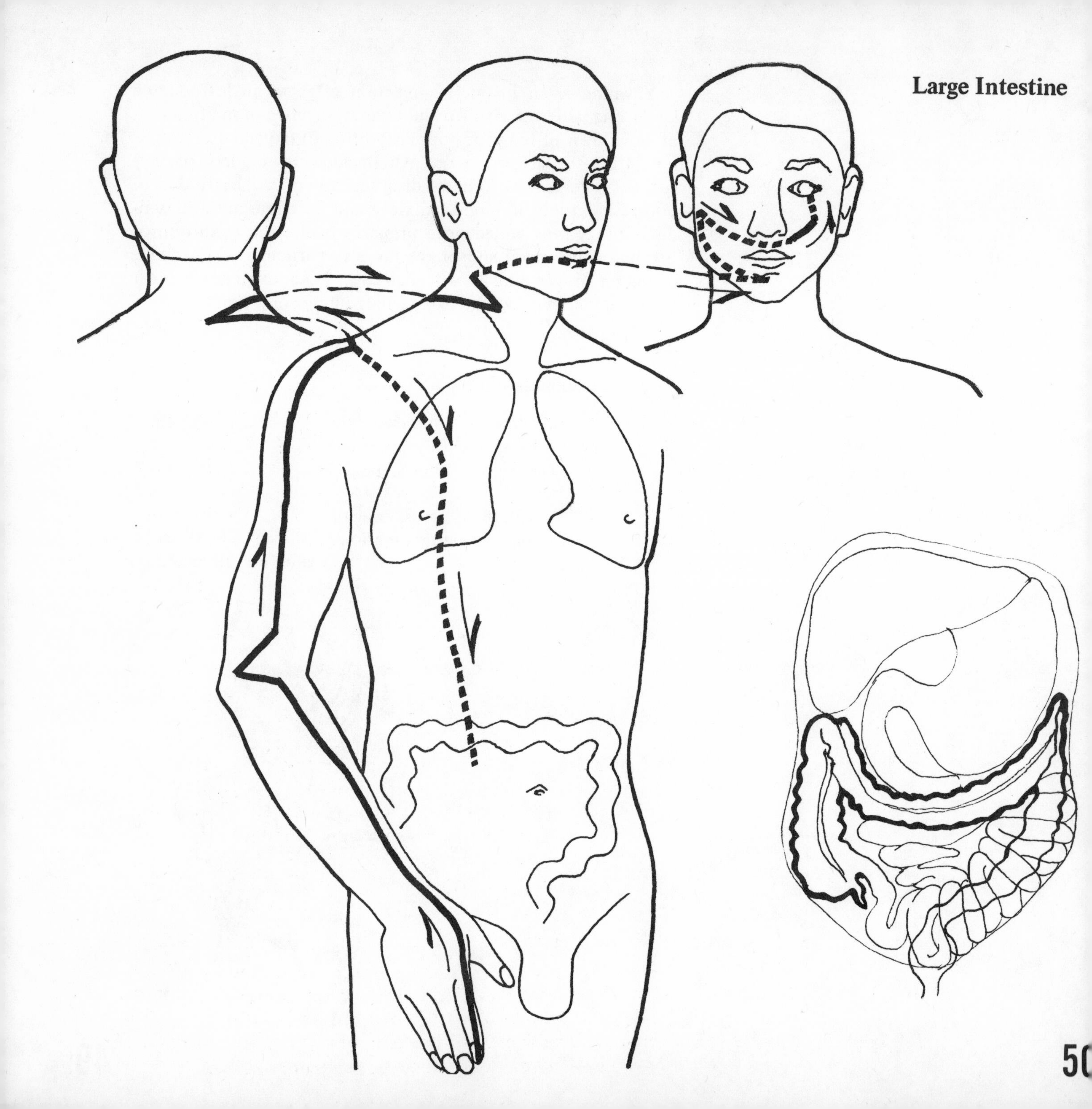

Large Intestine

Organ Structure and Function

The function of the organ is to eliminate the residues of digestion. The cleanliness of the organism, based on the complete discharge of toxins, depends on the efficient function of the large intestine.

In vegetarians, the first part of the ascending colon (cecum) on the right side of the cavity, is more importantly developed. This part contains ferments and digestants for the proper assimilation of cellulose (bran of grains, beans and other fibers).

The performance of the cecum is helped by consuming non-dairy lactic ferments such as naturally self-leavened bread, salt pickles and sauerkraut, miso paste, etc . . . which will accelerate or restore good ferments and reduce the type of microbial flora that produce gas.

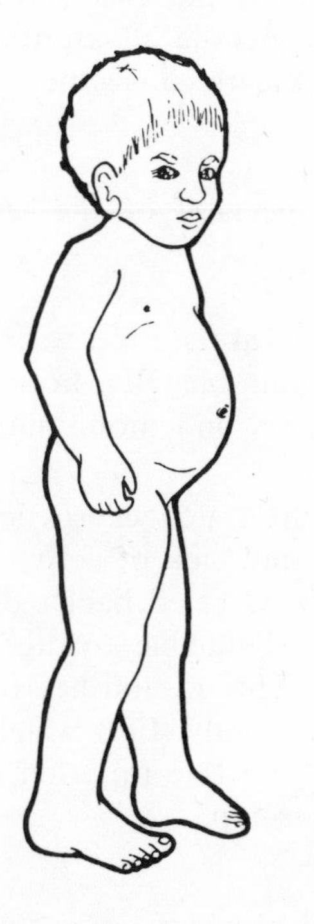

Meridian

The large intestine meridian begins in surface at the root of the index finger nail and courses centripetally on the external part of the arm. The outward end of the shoulder blade is crossed, then the meridian leaves the skin surface to connect with the lower part of the lung and the transverse colon. It then returns to the surface at a point under the chin side. From that point, the meridian is again buried deep within the area often referred to as the double chin and follows the lower row of dental roots, passing then to the upper line of teeth roots, crossing the front of the mouth to emerge on the skin surface at the facial point next to the nostrils.

Enemas -- Water Curse

One of the major functions of the last section of the large intestine is to remove water from fecal matter prior to discharge. To introduce any liquid into this part of the colon prevents molding and taxes the dehydrating function of the descending colon, resulting in loose bowels, hard to expell.

Requirements for optimum function

In the infant, deep abdominal massages and percussions create no painful reaction. Later on in life, a very small percentage of persons retain this advantage. The cause of pain in the large intestine (as well as in the small intestine and the stomach) are due to:

Chronic overeating which taxes the eliminative function.

Rapid eating without adequate chewing, forcing the intestines to perform extraordinary functions.

Eating of foods treated with antibiotics and preservatives which destroy intestinal flora in the small intestines and the cecum.

Emulsifiers which prevent the removal of water in the descending colon.

Sugar – which paralyses the digestion and the nervous system.

Enriched bread and flour products containing Dyox and Agene which are depressants for the nervous system and retard digestion.

Eating while under stress or in a state of anger.

Smoking – nicotine in the system produces violent peristaltic and intestinal spasms. Over a period of time, the drug's laxative effect becomes accepted and overcomes the natural triggering of emptying the colon. Thus a smoker who quits, no longer responds to nature calls but begins to fill the intestines with excess fecal matter.

Drugs -- most drugs act directly on the autonomic nervous system of the peristaltic muscles of the large intestine -- these drugs include all aspirins, coffee, sleeping pills, pain killers, anaesthetics, etc . . .

Lack of physical activity (especially of the legs and abdominal muscles).

Sitting down, riding in cars, elevators, etc . . . Recommended activities are: Riding bicycles, horses, walking, climbing stairs, ladders and mountains.

From the above, we sse that most malfunction causes are hypernutrition or poor selection of food and lack of activity. These causes begin in the first year of life. Overfed babies develop fat storage (adipose tissues) while still unable to digest solid food (cecum not functioning yet). This establishes for life, the size and number of fat cells in the body. Fast weight gain in early months always causes poor intestine function in later life even if chronic obesity does not develop.

Danger signals

Oversize colon or megacolon, intestinal blockage, parasites, enteritis and borborygmus, all stem from lack of attention to details outlined above. Danger signals which precede the actual disease are: Distended and painful belly, constipation, diarrhea, frequent nature calls, bad breath, gas, loss of memory and hemorrhoids.

Prevention Chewing food thoroughly will accomplish three roles:

1 - ANALYTICAL: The true taste and real or false value of each food will develop in chewing. At that stage, if the taste buds reject is as unacceptable for the body's need, overcoming the etiquette and spitting the food out becomes the first essential line of defense/prevention of disease.

2 - RESTRICT QUANTITY: Thorough chewing of any food will reduce the amount of intake while neutralizing the detrimental effect through salivation. It will also teach the palate and the taste buds to regain their selectivity.

3 - INDUCTIVE MASSAGE: The schematic of the Large Intestine meridian reveals that an important section of the subterranean channel lies along the root of the teeth (with connections to the lymph glands). Thus chewing affords possibly the best opportunity for inductive massage and stimulation of a chronically sluggish organ. It is well-known that when chewing stops as in fasting, emptying of colon also stops. Conversely, vigorous and thorough chewing promotes good peristaltic action and energetic nature calls.

Gas

The presence of gas (no less than 49 strains of anaerobic microbes produce it) and of foul-smelling stools are signs of large intestine malfunction. When gases have formed, attempting to suppress them or to halt their elimination is just as detrimental as halting the discharge of solid fecal matter, since, when held internally, these gases are converted into toxins such as: Cadaverine (ptomaine), putrescine, scatole, indole (putrefaction). When proper diet and intestinal functions are restored, all gas formation disappears.

The functions of the transverse and the descending colons are to complete the assimilation, to remove moisture and to mold the feces on their way to a temporary storage in the sigmoid flexure prior to final discharge. Movement of all fecal matter is assured in the healthy person by energetic peristaltic action of a large number of small peripheric muscles which contract involuntarily.

Relief of Pain and Symptoms

Deep direct massage of the abdomen should never be attempted when pain is present and the person has not changed his way of eating. Acupressure treatment of the following points will give temporary relief:

Constipation ...	... Tw 6
Diarrhea ...	... Se 36
Sharp colon pains ...	... Se 25
Loose feces (from excess water) ...	... Sp 15
Flatus (gas) Apply heat, moxabustion on ...	... Cvc 8

The Stomach

Function and Value

Ingested food is modified in the stomach into a digestible form, acceptable and non-toxic for the intestines. These modifications are biochemical by the action of gastric juices (hydrochloric acid + diastase) and peptones.

A mechanical action also takes place which attacks and partially dissolves the pectin which bonds vegetable fibers and the ligaments of meat tissues. In the stomach, only a small percentage of water-soluble proteins (vegetable and animal) have become peptones.

The lymph glands of the stomach lining also stimulate the spleen and the pancreas into producing various ferments such as trypsin and pancreatine. Some exocrine glands and the salivary glands of the mouth also secrete various amounts of fluids under the influence of the stomach. The transformation of food includes cooling or heating to a uniform compatible temperature so as to protect the small intestine, regulating the acidity of various foods. When food taken in is too irritating or incompatible, the opening of the stomach into the small intestine closes, holding the ingested poisonous substances until vomiting occurs. If the vomiting spasms are prevented by force, drinking antacids or liqueurs or by the taking of drugs to force the opening of the pylorus, this defense mechanism weakens and eventually accepts all food regardless of toxicity and temperature. The same closing of the pylorus will occur when the intestines are kept too cold, invalidated or compressed by poor posture. Emotions and cerebral malfunctions (such as hemorrhages) will cause the same trouble, going even as far as total stoppage. Finally, smokers mix in minute amounts of nicotine with saliva (even if not smoking at meal time – residues of nicotinic acid are always present) which move down with food into the stomach and inhibits the production of gastric juices in the stomach.

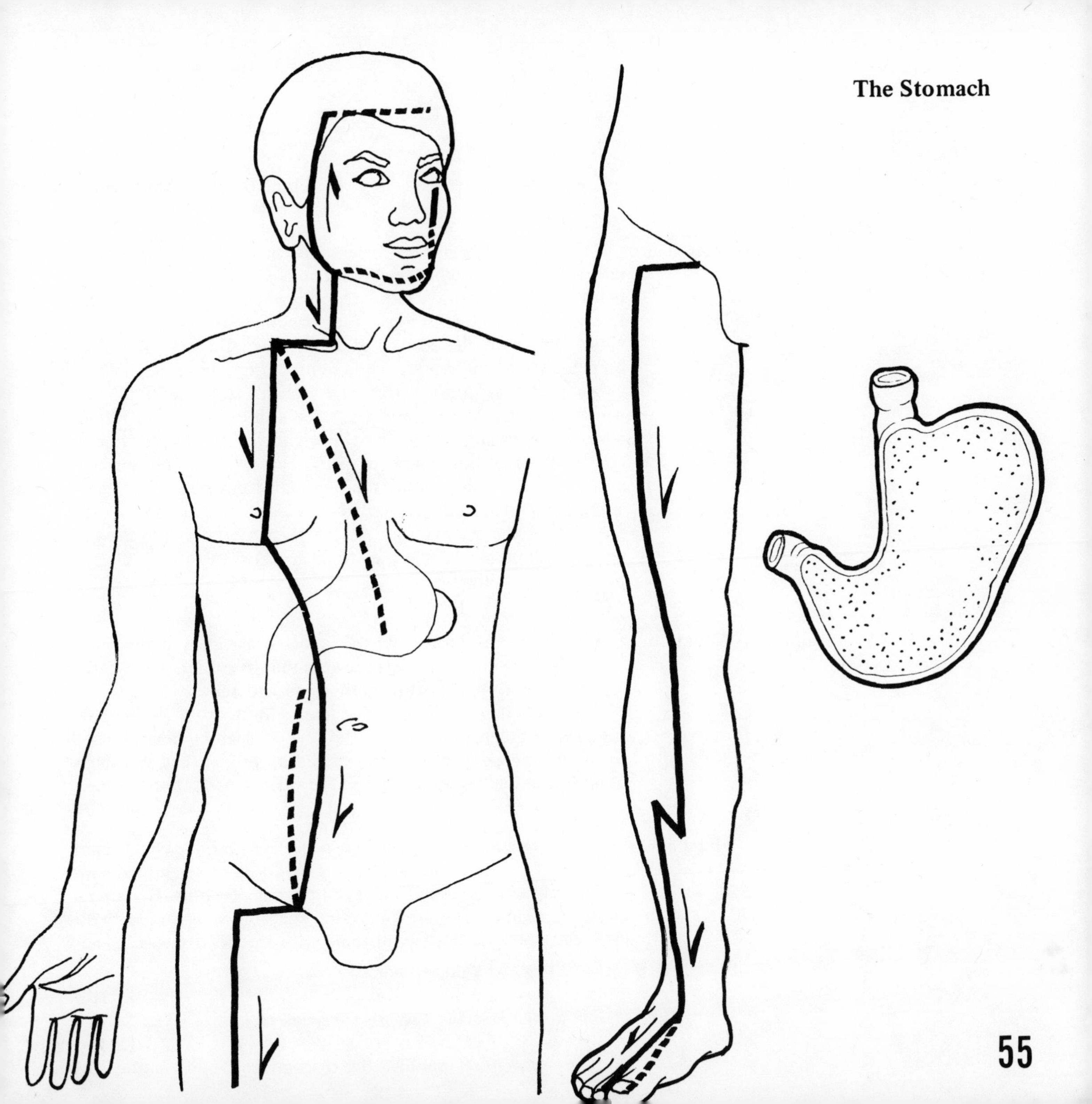

The Stomach

The Stomach Meridian

Pathway of the Meridian

The meridian begins in surface just below the eye and goes internal at the cheekbone where it runs along the upper row of teeth to the wisdom tooth returning along the roots of the lower teeth of the entire jaw, thus passing to the opposite side. Now coming to the surface at the edge of the jawbone, one branch rises to the temple while another goes down to the collarbone, at that point, an internal branch reaches the stomach while from the same point a surface section of the meridian courses downward on the chest down to the pubic area, where another internal link connects to the pylorus. From the surface point near the public bone, the meridian continues, in surface, along the forward outside part of the leg to end at the root of the nail of the second toe. At the level of the ankle, a connecting submeridian links the stomach meridian to the Spleen-Pancreas one at the big toe.

Traditional Structure

A study of the diagram of the stomach meridian shows, not only its surface points but also reveals that its subterranean path connects with the mouth, teeth roots and salivary glands, as well as with the organ itself and the pylorus. We also see that stomach problems: Gastritis, stenosis, dyspepsia, ptosis, volvurus and indigestion are easily solved by proper diet, mastication, limitation of quantity and proper mood at mealtime.

First aid

Direct massage of the stomach being even more painful than massage of the large intestine, it should not be attempted unless the patient has already changed his way of eating. However, inductive acupressure treatment of the following points will give temporary relief of symptoms until the next unwise meal.

stomach pains ...	... Cs 6
pylorus pains ...	... Lf 10
acute gastritis (dyspepsia) ...	... Se 21
excess gas ...	... Kr 14
general digestive discomfort ...	... Se 36

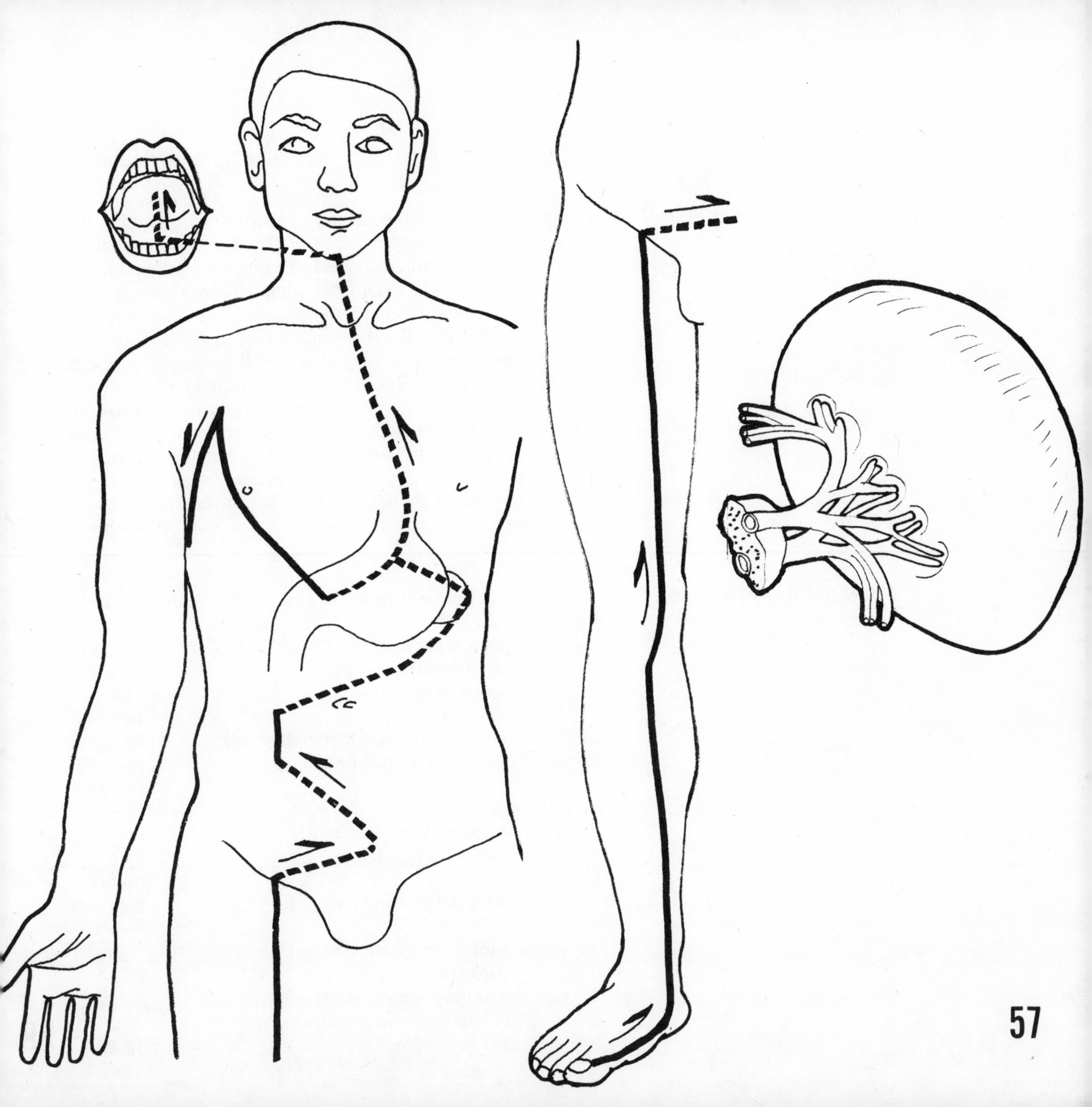

The Spleen/Pancreas

The Meridian System

Beginning at the big toenail and of centripetal direction, the meridian courses the internal face of the foot. The third pressure point of the meridian is called "Extreme Pallor" and refers to the condition of white skin associated with iron anemia, constipation and colonic bleeding, the signs of a body without defenses. The meridian follows the inside part of the leg up to the groin. The meridian leaves the surface of the skin and connects internally with the gonads (reproductive organs) and returns in surface for a short link to plunge inward again in order to control the spleen and the stomach. The subterranean branch rises up to the muscles controlling the tongue. Another subterranean branch issues from the pylorus and emerges in surface at the chest to terminate at the armpit. Both the surface last pressure point and the internal ending at the tongue, connect with the next meridian of the heart.

Relief of Pain and Symptoms

For inductive finger massage treatment, the following points are given:

Kidney and ureter infections,	
cystitis (in man) . . .	. . . Sp 6
cystitis (in woman) . . .	. . . Cvc 2 to 6
Asthenia, debility, uterus inflammation . . .	. . . Sp 2
Genital inflammation (man or woman) . . .	. . . Sp 6, 9 and 16
Impotency in man . . .	. . . Sp 9
Frigidity and sterility in woman . . .	. . . Sp 16
To trigger earlier menstruation . . .	. . . Sp 6 (only)
Menstrual irregularities and pain . . .	. . . Sp 8 and Sp 10
Parasites in intestines, liver, bile and pancreas ailments . . .	. . . Sp 14
Bronchial and lung congestions, jaundice, pneumonia and all diseases of the lower esophagus . . .	. . . Sp 17

The Organ of Spleen-Pancreas -- Function

Guardian of the body through a complex system of immunity, the spleen is the keeper of magnetic iron and hemoglobin; it is the regulator of red blood cells. Part of the immune system which patrols the body through the lymphatic vessels, the spleen, along with the thymus, lymph nodes and the lymphocyte cells, produces 100 million trillion of antibodies. These antibodies are triggered into action by viruses and bacteria and by protein molecules, hormones, enzymes, hemoglobin and cell walls. To perform these jobs, they have the gift of instantaneous adaptability and expendability. In a healthy being, they can do any job of defense, even those which appear unsurmountable.

It is the presence of antibodies and their performance which enable the body to remain in harmony with its environment. The multi-faceted functions of the antibodies include that of acceptance, they could thus be more aptly named "probodies". It has been stated that the immune system does not recognize the antigens that are part of one's own body. This self-tolerance is the constructive part of the spleen system, it enables us to function smoothly within the environment. The immune system learns its self-tolerance in embryonic life and its continued learning depends on its healthy condition; it performs well or not at all. The potential response of a lymphocyte can either be antagonistic (it will then destroy) or synergistic (cooperative) with other antibodies to enhance the "welcome guest" effect. A given foreign antigen will be recognized more and more and, provided the system's response remains in good order, accepted by all antibodies. A parallel may be drawn between the lymph system and the nervous system. Both are capable of receiving and transmitting signals, these can either "inhibit" or "promote". The two systems reach most areas of the body and are linked together by the "Brain-nerve-governor" meridian which separates the two from each other.

The pancreas has a variety of functions: Supplying diastases and pancreatic juices to the stomach and intestine for the digestion of food. It also supplies a secretion to the liver which regulates its sugar production. Malfunction of the pancreas, taxes the liver and allows an excessive amount of sugar to pass into the body. In time of chaotic nutrition, the spleen-pancreas system bears an extra burden which visibly affects its first pressure points, evidenced by enlarged big toes, bunions and odd-shaped toenails.

Danger Signals

Tendency to sleep during the day, bad memory, loss of alertness and understanding, dull legs, anemia and cerebral exhaustion, brain fag, inconsistent appetite and craving for sweets. Note: Excessive imagination may be a sign of stagnant energy of the meridian. It is to be calmed. If heat is felt at the reflex point Sp 9, the spleen-pancreas is in excess.

Malfunction of the small intestine can be detected early by the inability to turn the head 180° from left to right and vice-versa, by spontaneous pain in the lower abdomen (Cv 4 pressure point), pains in the throat and the shoulders, stiff neck and development of double chin. Abcesses in the mouth and in the upper lip (cold sores), fullness in the chest sometimes accompanied by fever and perspiration. In extreme cases yellow tinged eyeballs constantly jumping about, deafness, swollen cheeks, stiff and painful shoulder also occur.

Menstruation

Irregularities of menstrual flow is common amongst modern women. The widespread use of air conditioning which unseasonally lowers the temperature of the water in the body is one cause. Several other causes ranging from the Pill, hormones, drugs, artificial cooling drinks and foods – up to artificial synthetic clothing and lack of activity – have drastically affected the circulation in the female body. Connected by the kidneys to the uterus, the menstrual flow mechanism is also affected by the mechanism of watergate.

Late and Early Menstruation Triggering Points

The release of blood periodically, relieves a woman of Yang and keeps her Yin (feminine). In order for this Yang to leave, it is important to avoid extremes of Yin on the days just preceeding the period. Thus, any Yin food, ice cold water or food and even washing the hair (Yin on top of the body directly opposite to the womb) causes a retention or delay of the monthly flow.

When menstruation has not come by the 29th day, treatment of this acupoint will trigger earlier menstruation: Sp6 (Spleen-pancreas).

If menstruation occurs too early; strong, deep and slow massage on the acupoint of Gvb. 34 will serve to delay the next cycle around. (Gall bladder 34 is located on the external part of the leg just below the knee.) Should an uninformed or too eager person treat both points at once, the effects will cancel each other and no change in periodicity will result.

First Aid Points

Severe low back pain at or near the time of menstruation . . . . . . Lf 8

Sensation similar to the uterus being pulled down . . . massage Sp 9

When the same pain appears to flow upward in the uterus . . . . . . treat both Cs 6 and Sp 4 (together or one after the other)

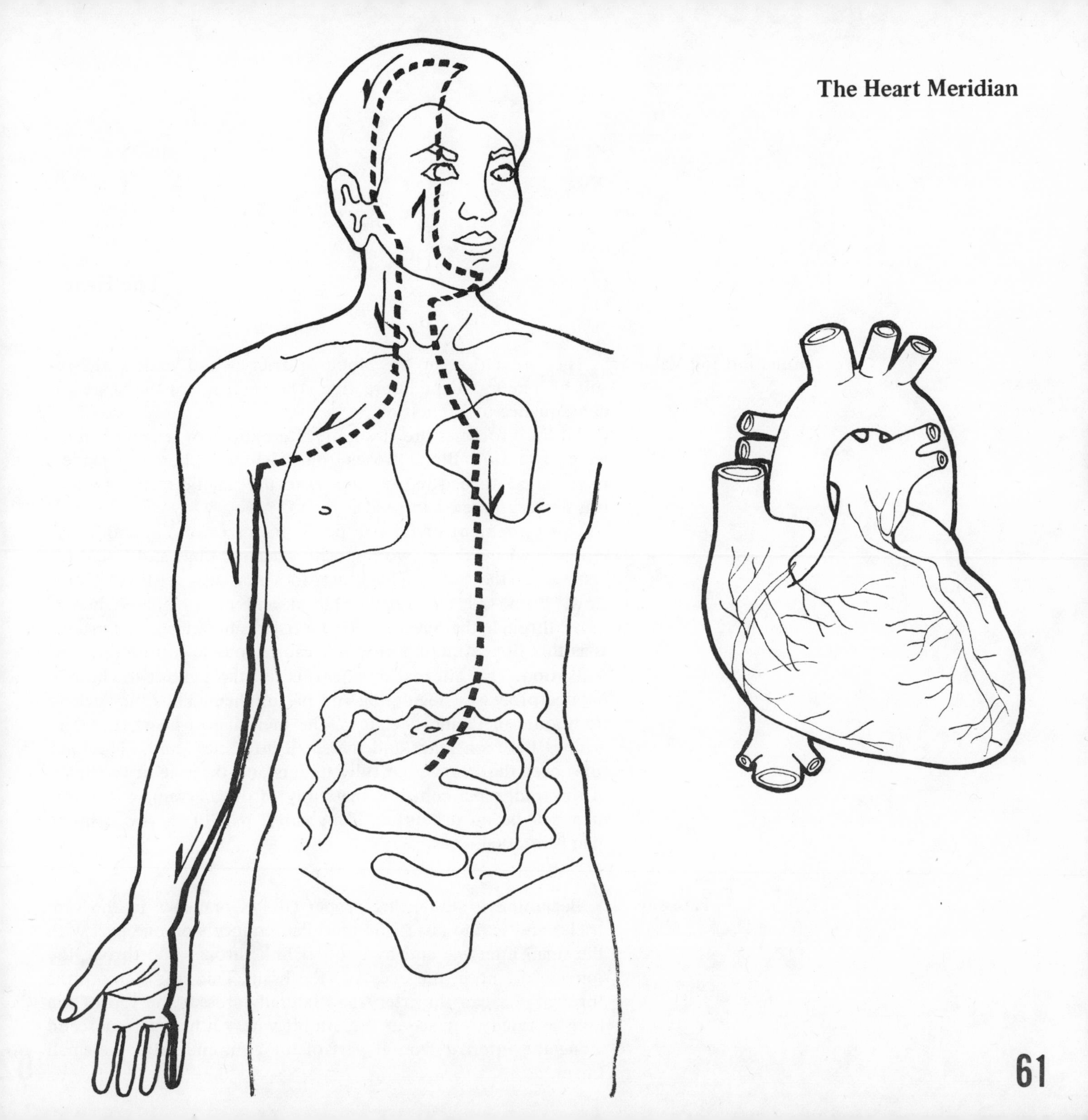
The Heart Meridian

The Heart

Function and Value

The circulation of the blood in arteries and veins is the result of Yin and Yang interaction. The pulsating of the heart is a consequence of circulation.

All life processes are rhythmic alternations of tension and release of tension. Blood moves from the lungs (where it is made--oxygenated–turned red--yangized) to the small intestine (where it is deoxygenated--yinnized).

This movement of flow responds to forces of Yin and Yang, represented by these two opposite organs, Lungs and Small Intestine, as the poles. The heart does not beat without blood flow. Both the oxygenated blood and deoxygenated blood move through the heart creating tension and release of tension. It is this flow stimulation which causes muscle contraction and relaxation. This alternation (beat) is felt throughout the body's organic processes, regulating and pacing them. Thus the ancient traditional medicine declares "The meridian of heart rules the arteries between lungs and the small intestine", and "The lung rules over the heart". To fully understand the role of the heart in the traditional concept, the study of the diagram of its meridian will be most helpful. The greatest part of the heart meridian is internal.

Pathway

Beginning in the heart proper (it has branches in the ventricles and in the atria) the meridian connects on one part with the small intestine and by another link through the throat, the tongue, the nose, the eyes and the brain. This link then returns through the carotid artery and laterally crosses the top of the lung to finally surface at the armpit where it begins to descend along the internal frontal part of the arm, ending at the small finger.

Danger Signals

The heart controls the mind. If the heart is weak, like a ruler without power, it invites revolt. When a multitude of body areas are troubled and the focus of the problem cannot be pinpointed, it means that Ki (both internal and external) is not flowing properly in the heart meridian.

The subterranean meridian courses through the eyes. When the eyes show red lines, the heart is weak. Areas of skin on the forehead and below the eyes as well as on the inside of the upper arms will also take on a red color when the circulation of the blood is deficient.

With the roots of the heart in the tongue, a fluent speech denotes a good heart, but persons who speak too much and without pause or who stutter and have difficulty speaking in public (shy and blushing) display signs of malfunction of the heart and circulation. A person with a weak heart works strenuously and fast to conceal its weakness.

The heart is considered the seat of spiritual faculties and the ruler of wisdom and good judgement. If a lack of keenness and understanding is apparent, the heart has insufficient circulation of energy.

Relief of Pain and Symptoms.

The pressure point where the meridian emerges (Hc 1) must always remain dry. If perspiration is present, treat for heart hyperactivity: Hc 6 and Hc 7.

Fear, anxiety, mental exhaustion and phobias . . . . . . Hc 3

Enlarged heart, inflammation of heart, crying, hysteria . . . . . . Hc 4

Eye congestion, irritation and dizziness . . . . . . Hc 5

Perspiration (especially at night), oppression . . . . . . Hc 6

Hyperactive heart, ulcers of small intestine, epilepsy . . . . . . Hc 7

Pharyngitis, tonsilitis . . . . . . Hc 5 and Hc 7

Blocked kidneys . . . . . . Hc 8

Pleuresy . . . . . . Hc 9

An Anecdote

In the history of China, there came a time when the medicine of herb teas and specific medications began to disappoint the people. It was then that the Emperor said:

"I hereby decree that all teas and remedies be abolished in favor of acupuncture. Those remedies and herb teas in use today, so far, have only made my people more miserable than they were before, to such a distressing point, that I can no longer collect taxes."

A traditional anecdote is still told today in Chinese medical circles: "One evening, having dined too well, the Emperor found himself becoming very ill. Calling his chamberlain, he directed him to summon the best physician of the capital. Earlier, an imperial edict had obliged every doctor to hang above his door one lantern for every one of his patient who had died in treatment. There were in the city certain doors which were illuminated by countless lanterns and the physicians would rather have done without them. . . ! The chamberlain went through the streets of the city and came back after a few hours leading a rather young-looking physician.

The Emperor asked,–"Is this the best doctor of the city? And how come it took you so long to find him?"

"Sire, said the chamberlain, "I ran all over the capital, horrified by the bright illuminations displayed on the doors of the most celebrated physicians. Finally, I located this man, perhaps quite young, but his merit is, that he had only one lantern hung outside his door!"

The Emperor said,–"This is incredible, you so young and in this whole city the only one who counts only one death in his clientele?"

Finally the young physician spoke,–"Yes, you Majesty, this is absolutely true. In all legality, I am honored to need only one lantern lit above my door. But I have opened my cabinet only yesterday!"

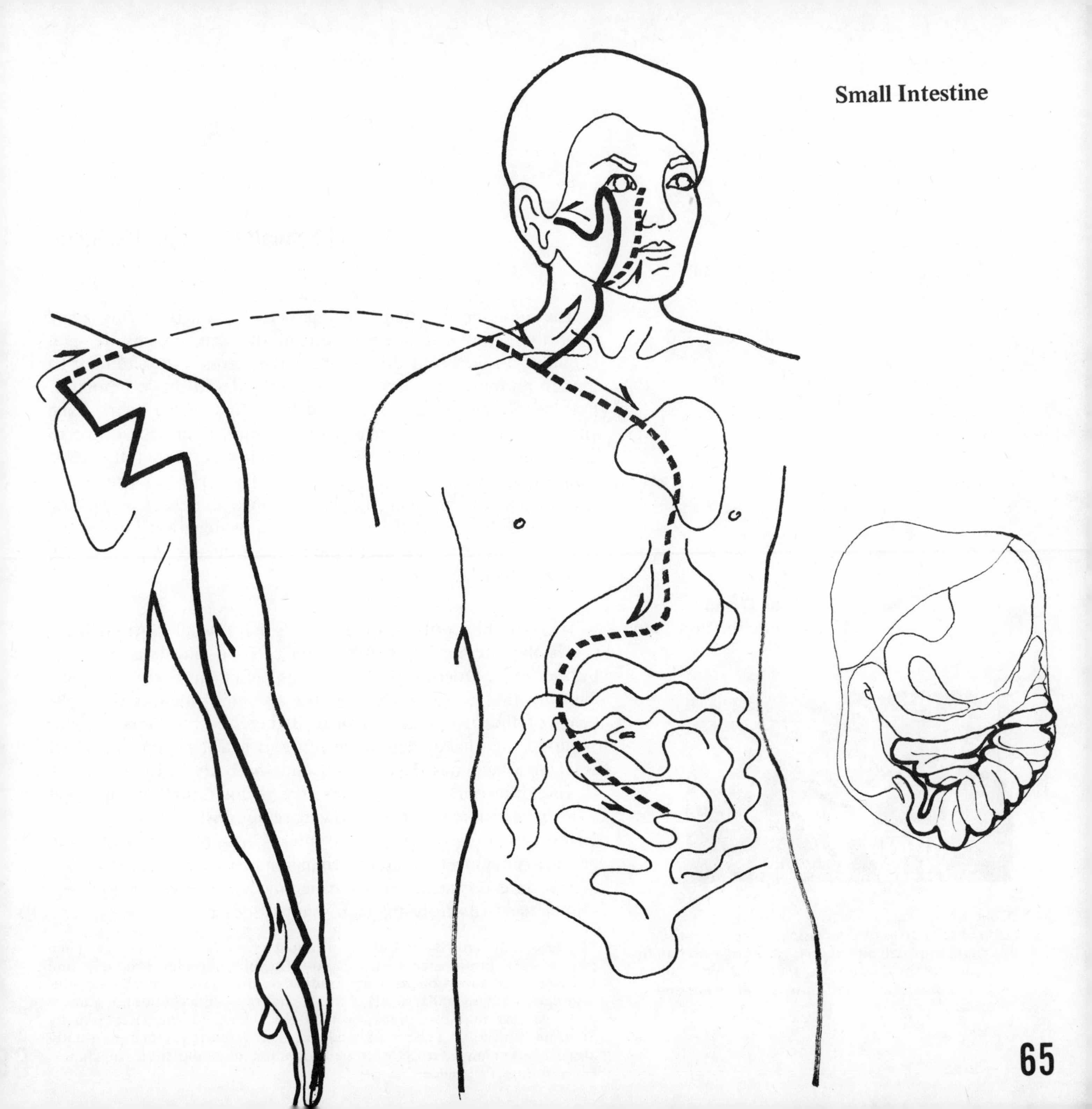
Small Intestine

The Small Intestine Meridian

The meridian of small intestine begins at the little finger and rises along the rear internal face of the arm, crosses the rear shoulder blade. From this back point it crosses the shoulder to a point above the collarbone where it divides into two branches: One deeply enters the body and links first to the heart, from there it rises, still internally to the throat, then back down to the diaphragm, stomach and small intestine. From the same point in surface above the collarbone, the other link rises along the outside of the neck, courses through the cheeks, reaching the outside corner of the eye, then returns downward under the jawbone corner to run up to the front of the ear opening where it enters the internal ear.

The Organ Function and Value

The portable roots of man is the small intestine. Alone it assumes the chemical transformation of food and its absorption by the body. Oriental thought states "Man and Earth not two" meaning that the condition of the second influences the well-being of the first. When earth or its ingested products become polluted, sterilized, demineralized and artificial, the intestinal tract also becomes degenerated and the body follows suit.

The intestine accomplishes the transformation of food with the assistance of the following secretions:
Erepsin (peptidase enzymes) – enterokinase (changing zymogen into enzymes) – maltase (changing maltose into dextrose) – invertase (yeast, changing cane sugar into invert sugar) – and lactase* (hydrolysing lactose into glucose).

Colic
One of the curses of Overeating.
Here, the "bell-pain-dwarfs" torture a woman by choking her small intestines, toxic, chemicalized and irritating foods also contribute to colic pains and diseases.

*Lactase: This enzyme is lacking in humans over two years of age. Their physiological intolerance to the lactose (in milk and milk products) and the continued ingestion of dairy products is the cause of many intestinal disorders. Lactose (milk sugar) is a carbohydrate (disaccharide) of glucose and galactose requiring breakdown by the lactase enzyme. Research by Stanford University School of Medicine discovered that lactase is totally absent in human adults. Continued ingestion of undigestible substances leads to intestinal cancer.

Small Intestine All of the above, except the last one (see footnote) are produced continuously by the small intestine and remain present only when the diet is harmonious and consists of unchemicalized staples. If the diet has been supplied by artificial and commercially prepared products, then depopulation of flora has taken place. Repopulation of enzymes and ferments and rebuilding of the intestinal cells will be required.

Danger Signals

Malfunction of the small intestine can be detected early by the inability to turn the head 180° from left to right and vice-versa, by spontaneous pain in the lower abdomen (Cv 4 pressure point), pàins in the throat and the shoulders, stiff neck and the development of double chin. Abcesses in the mouth and in the upper lip (cold sores), fullness in the chest sometimes accopanied by fever and perspiration. In extreme cases yellow tinged eyeballs constantly jumping about, deafness, swollen cheeks, stiff and painful shoulders also occur.

Skin irritation and dry skin . . .	. . . Sig 3
Deafness and ringing in the ear . . .	. . . Sig 5, 16, 17, 19
All diseases of the eye	. . . Sig 6
Congestion in the head and neck, nervous breakdown, melancholy, dizziness . . .	. . . Sig 7
Bronchitis, asthma, pharyngitis (impotency, early ejaculations) . . .	. . . Sig 14
Spasms in the throat, poor vision, jaundice . . .	. . . Sig 15
Otitis (inflammation of ear) and deafness . . .	. . . Sig 19

Coffee – *Caffeine* is a drug which belongs to the amphetamine group, so are the related drugs: Theophylline and theobromine (3-7 Dimethyl-Xamthine) found in tea and cocoa respectively. In addition to the well-known destructive effects of these alcaloids on the central nervous system: Cardiac arrythmia, cephalea, insomnia, unrealistic euphoria and increase in blood pressure, it is important to note that cocoa, tea and coffee bring into the organism quantities of *purine* which have been proven to cause gastric troubles, ulcers, chronic indigestion, colon stasis and diverticulosis, chronic indigestion, nausea and vomiting. The aromatic *flavor* oils in coffee can cause diarrhea and the tannin in tea induce constipation, both contain drugs which will accelerate the burning of food and simulate an increase of energy; these, when coupled with the alcaloids cause a definite breakdown of the large intestine function. Cafeone, the major aroma of coffee decomposes during the roasting process *thermocracking* into cancer-causing compounds ("Prostate Cancer and Coffee Consumption" Dr. Takahashi, Japan.)

The Bladder

The bladder is the watergate of the body; it collects the urine excreted by the kidneys and holds it between urinations. It also regulates the flow of water, beginning in the brain and its surface, it is instrumental in the formation of valleys in the brain surface in order to develop intelligence.* Highly developed brain always shows deep valleys. Excess water collects in all parts of the body, swelling various organs and affecting the organs of sight, hearing, taste and smell. Many of the pressure points of the bladder meridian are treated to correct and regulate the flow of water.

Danger Signals of Impending Bladder Ailments

Pain in the back of the neck, insomnia, pain in the backbone, violent pain in the kidney area and the ankles (Achille's tendon), myopia, unsharp vision, itching eyes, runny eyes and sensitivity to cold and wind.

Signs of Acute Diseases of the Bladder

Headaches, especially the top of the head, hemorrhoids, pain in upper jaws, mental unbalance, crying spells, runny nose and eyes, pains in the back, in the anus, in the ankle and the entire foot.

First Aid Points

Congested kidneys, eye diseases,
exophtalmos . . . . . . Bv 1
Trachea and bronchial infections,
pneumonia, influenza,
coughing, nasal drip and tonsilitis . . . . . . Bv 12
Respiratory illnesses, nose ailments,
vomiting . . . . . . Bv 13

*In infants, the surface of the brain is smooth at the beginning of life, just as the earth in primeval times. Action of water on earth washes soil away to create mountains, valleys and interesting terrain. The human brain, through water control, massage, finger touching, loving contact and breath of adults also acquires interesting valleys and develops intelligence.

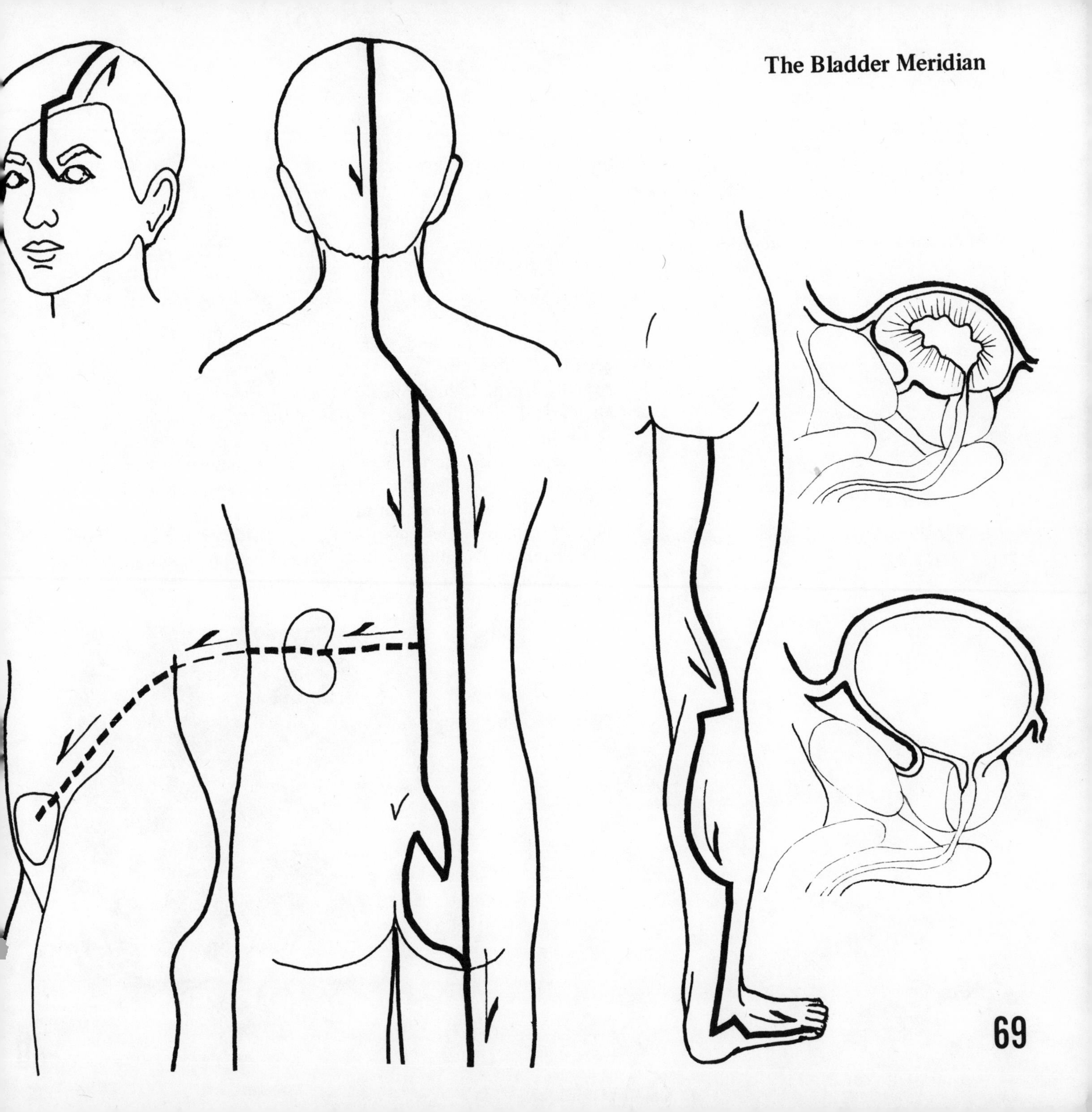

The Meridian -- Surface and Internal Location

The bladder meridian begins at the internal corner of the eye, rising vertically across the forhead. It contours the skull and descends the back of the neck to the upper back where it divides into two branches, both in surface and both parallel to the rear median line of the body. The branch closest to the middle descends to the sacrum and at the lumbar region it penetrates internally to the kidney and the bladder. From the sacrum, again the surface interior branch courses along the rear of the thigh to reach the hollow fold of the rear of the knee. The external most outward surface meridian penetrates internally at the point of the buttock and joins the interior surface meridian at the knee fold. The meridian now continues singly, turning to the external part of the lower leg, contours the outside of the ankle bone and terminates at the small toe. From a point near the heel a linkage joins to the first point of the kidney meridian at the plantar area of the foot.

THE RAIN DRAGON.

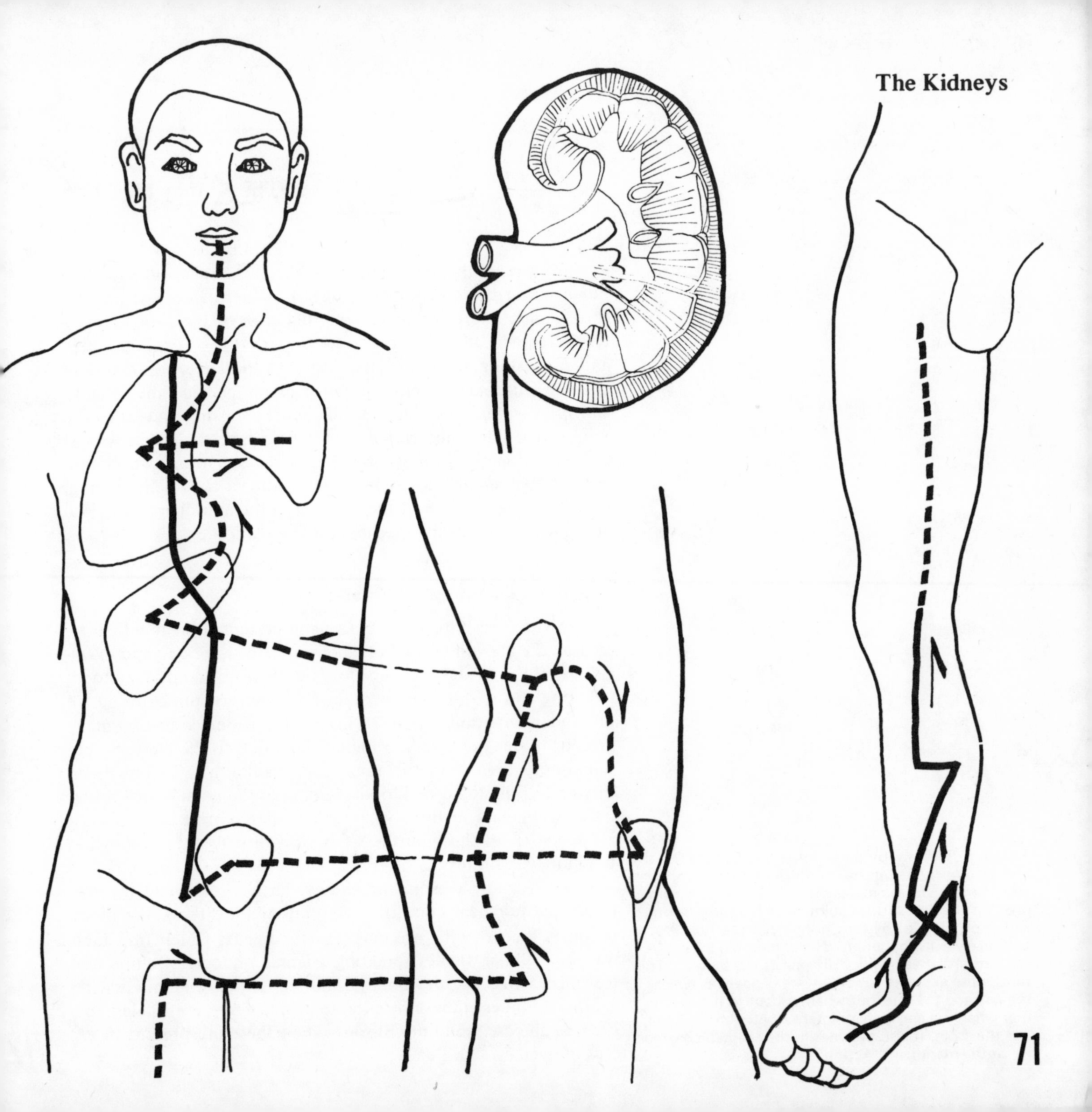

The Kidney Meridian

Pathway

The start of this meridian, is unlike the others, since it does not begin at the corner of a nail but at the plantar (sole of the foot) area*. It crosses to the internal edge of the foot, slightly to the top of the foot, contours the interior side of the ankle and rises along the leg to the knee. At the knee, the meridian becomes internal to join the point of the coccyx, the kidneys and follows the ureter to the bladder. From the bladder to the pubic area, a deep internal branch connects to the pubis. Now it surfaces from the genitals and rises to the collarbone. A secondary internal branch leads from the kidneys to the liver, lung, heart and tongue. It is at the heart, that the meridian of the kidneys connects with the meridian of Circulation/Sex.

Function - Traditional Viewpoint

The kidney is a highly selective and perfected organ which regulates the movements of organic waters of the body and extracellular fluids. The secondary function is filtration of the blood, selecting and reabsorbing proteins, glucose, sodium chloride, all oligo elements and much of the water. Kidneys do not make urea or urate, the artery bringing the blood to the kidneys contains more urea than the renal vein leading away from them. Further, an increase of blood pressure in the renal artery brings only an increase in the concentration of the urine but does not influence at all the quantity of it: this dispells the notion that the kidney is simply "a filter".

When, for any reason, the kidneys cannot select and regulate (from pathological condition or tying of the tubes), the blood becomes loaded with noxious waste elements which find their way to cellular tissues, creating edemas or local swelling and toxemia. While the detrimental matter is totally eliminated by healthy kidneys, they also excrete some of the useful elements such as glucose, sodium chloride when these are present in excess of need.

*It is a fact known by the scholars that the start of the meridian really lies at the nail (but internally) and that the energy surfaces only at the sole. Traditional names used for the first surface point are: "Bubbling Spring" and also "Flooded by the Spring", but the *Tzen Yuan* dictionary calls that point "High Mountain Spring", generating a stream which disappears in a valley". This third sense explains not only what happens between the nail and the sole, but what is about to happen further when the energy goes internal between the knee and the groin. It also preludes to the energetic character of the meridian: "Action".

The Kidneys

Danger Signals

The overall face color is black particularly the forehead and the area below the eyes which is also puffy. Bones become weak as a result of kidney contraction. The root of the tongue becomes coated, air collects in the pelvis, disrupting the urination and all sexual functions.

△ **Signs of excess energy**: Bloated abdomen, swelling of parts of the body, dark brown urine color (coffee color, bloody), change in pattern of urination, frequency, time of day or night, aversion to speak, bursts of activity with intense energy output, cannot stop working, insomnia. Sudden outburst of perspiration after consumption of food, sensation of heaviness throughout body.

▽ **Signs of deficiency of energy**: Timidity, fear, impatience, suspicious and undecisive, lack of will, absence of sex drive, easily surprised, groaning (sometimes inaudible), frequent yawns, snoring at night and insomnia, most tranquil and inactive before sundown, awakens early and sleeplessness in early hours.

Treatment and Care

When stimulated, the filtration of the kidneys is reduced and its secretion increased. In case of albuminuria (presence of albumin in the urine), pollakiuria (frequent urination) and polyuria (excessive quantity); stimulation of the kidneys by light, rapid and short duration massage is desirable. The same stimulation will have a definite tonifying effect on the adrenal cortex and the thyroid. This explains why the superior Oriental physician finds a definite mental influence, a personality trait, in connection with the kidneys, it is verified that when diseased kidneys are tonified, the will and decisiveness of the patient is strengthened.

To calm or diminish the energy in the kidneys increases the filtration but assures more secretion as required in case of kidney congestion. Some of the symptoms of Kidney congestion are anuria (absence of urination) contracted and painful kidneys, fever without sweat, night perspiration, hypertension, head and neck congestion, feels very coldish, lack of energy, fainting from weakened condition, sleepiness, loss of memory, very painful headache, dumb (no will to speak), spitting blood with coughing, distended belly, pain on each side of navel, icy cold feet up to the knees and cannot remain seated or much less in the seiza posture (sitting on heels).

What is Urine?

The combination of undesirable and/or surplus useful elements are dissolved and excreted in the form of a water solution: this is urine. Kidneys secrete water only when this liquid reaches a level above a certain threshold in the blood stream. Urination volume will diminish when there is fever in the body. In chronic illnesses or as an indication of fatal diseases, the volume of urine sharply decreases or stops altogether. When convalescence occurs, urination resumes in normal volume. Lack of urine flow with attending increase in blood volume tires the heart. This calls for a reduction of water and salt.

First Aid Points

In women: hard and swollen belly simulating pregnancy, cannot urinate, drooping of sexual organs, crooked uterus, sterility.

In man and woman: Inflamation of sexual organs, hard lumps in belly, and all sorts of hernias: for these treat the first point of . . . . . . Kr 1

At the sole of the foot, while toes are bent under (flexed) head and neck congestion, nightime perspiration, unvoluntary erection, polymenorrhea (frequent menstruation), vulvar pruritus (itching of vulva), pharyngitis, tonsilitis . . . . . . treat Kr 2

Retention of urine, bladder spasms, hysteria, insomnia, diabetes . . . . . . treat Kr 5, 6 and 7

Stomach troubles, nervous breakdown, jaundice . . . . . . treat Kr 8, 9, and 10

Impotency, ovarian infection, eye congestion . . . . . . treat Kr 11 and 12

Stomach ache, colic, swelling of belly, gas, constipation or diarrhea, ascites (fluid in the peritoneal cavity) . . . . . . treat Kr 14

The above acupoint is also treated when water is detected by palpation of the large intestine, watery feces, intolerable pain in the navel.

Sexual Ability and the Kidneys

The kidneys call to life that which is dormant (the gonads). In the sex act, the kidneys excrete and make the essence of the whole body pass into the semen or the ovum. The close association of the kidneys with the sex organs (testicles and ovaries) as well as the adrenals (the cortex and the medulla) make impotence and frigidity a condition brought about by malfunction (over or under secretion) of the kidneys and of "sexual ability". In either case, the heart and the blood circulation are heavily taxed as they attempt to maintain organic water and hemoglobin in balance.

Circulation/Sex Meridian

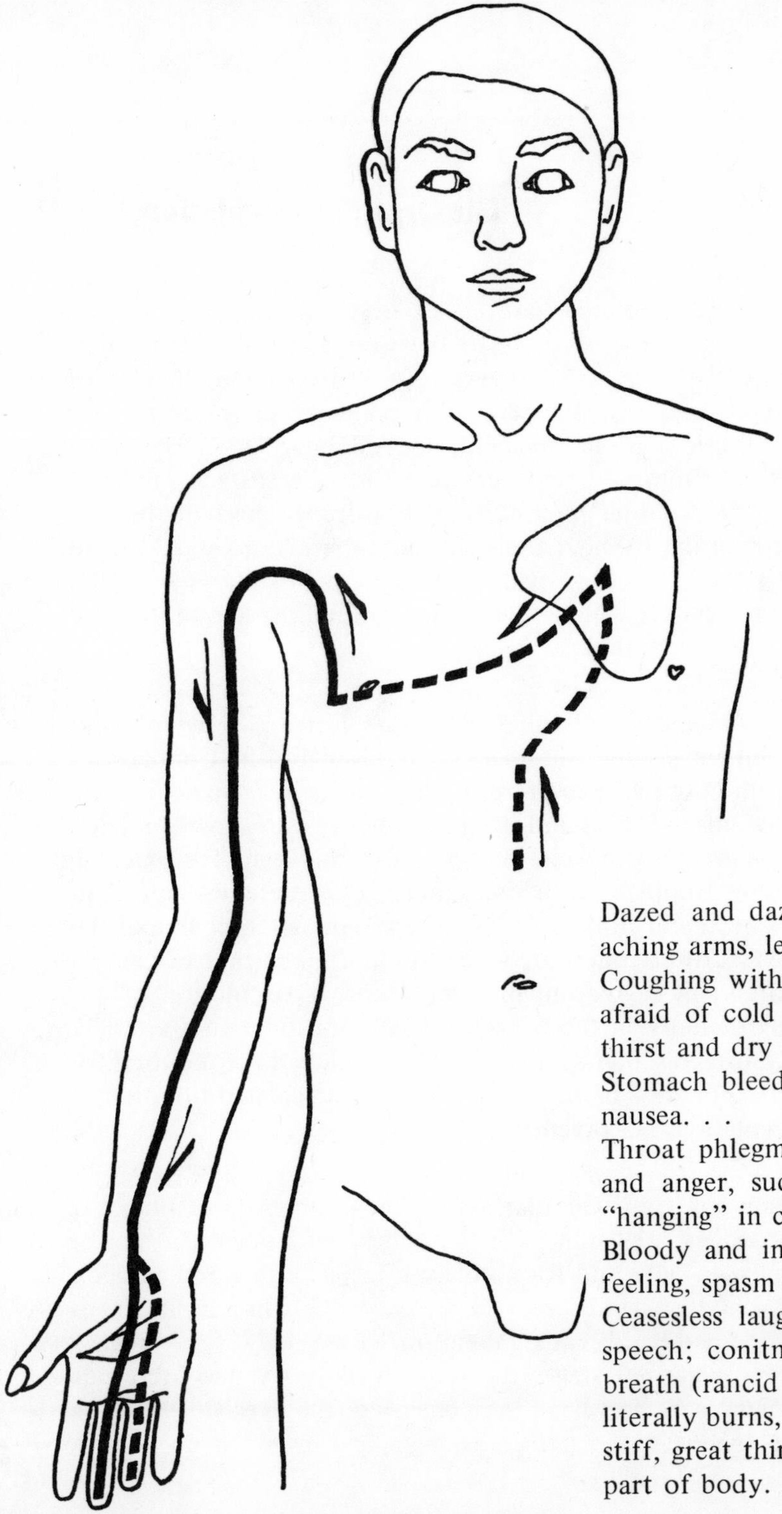

First Aid Acupoints

Dazed and dazzled feeling, blurry vision, swelling in armpits, aching arms, legs and arms paralyzed. . . . . . treat Sc 1

Coughing with aches in chest, back and arms; person is shy or afraid of cold and wind, the heart feels heavy, there is much thirst and dry mouth, vomit phlegm. . . . . . treat Cs 2 and 3

Stomach bleeding, fear of all persons (even friendly relatives), nausea. . . . . . treat Cs 4

Throat phlegm, strangling apoplexy, epilepsy, sudden madness and anger, sudden loss of speech, inflamed heart, heart feels "hanging" in chest. . . . . . treat Cs 5

Bloody and inflamed eyes, soreness in belly with "full" chest feeling, spasm and constricted elbows. . . . . . treat Cs 6

Ceaseless laughter, patient cackles, cries or moans; rambling speech; conitnuous anger, perpetual frown, mouth sores, bad breath (rancid smell), no feeling in hands, palms very hot, body literally burns, fever without perspiration, tongue is swollen and stiff, great thirst, heart is inflamed, cannot turn or twist upper part of body. . . . . . treat Cs 8 and 9

The Organ of Circulation/Sex

Meridian Pathway

The meridian of Circulation/Sex begins internally at the solar plexus with connections to the liver and the gall bladder, from there it rises to the heart before surfacing at the side of the nipple area, the first acupoint on the skin (prior to that point, all stimulations are made by inductive Do-in breathing exercises). From the first surface point, the surface meridian rises to the shoulder then descends the frontal part of the arm and crosses the palm, it then contours the major finger to end at the root of its fingernail. A secondary link starts from the wrist and sends a connecting branch to the first acupoint of the Triple Warmer meridian.

The Organ of Circulation Sex Function

The fundamental circulation of Life Force (Ki) which connects and unites the inner organs is ruled by the Circulation/Sex. It functions also to prevent entry of the infectious diseases. As such, this meridian and its inner functions are closely related to the heart; both possess the same external signs for signaling impending troubles, both use similar suggestions for optimum performance and both originate in the same internal area of the chest. A further function of Circulation/Sex is that of general superintendent regulating the whole body's circulation of energy, particularly in the liver and the gall bladder and generally in the entire vascular system. Providing the energy required for good performance of the sex organs is an associated function of the Circulation/Sex organ.

Danger Signals

At the onset, the Circulation/Sex organ flares up in a burst of energy. Signs are fullness in the chest and sides, the person laughs excessively and for no reason, facial color is red and congested, palm of hands are very warm, swelling in armpits, incessant thirst and bad breath (rancid smell).

In the advanced stage, the heart feels heavy and laborious, the lungs, neck and head are congested, the eyesight weakens, sudden madness, the person is angry and cross for no or little reason.

The internal branch of the Triple Warmer meridian begins at the collarbone, joins the heart and from there connects with the digestive and the reproductive organs, its return, still internal, is on the same pathway.

SOL HOUSE 301 KEELE ST.

The Triple Warmer

Pathway

The meridian of the Triple Warmer begins at the root of the little fingernail ascending along the backside of the arm up to the shoulder just under the shoulder blade. From this point, the meridian crosses over to the front of the shoulder where it continues internally below the collarbone to join the heart, the cardiac plexus, the lungs, stomach, pylorus and the bladder. The meridian then rises to emerge in surface at an acupoint just above the collarbone, then reaches the neck, the mastoid and contours the rear of the ear. Passing to the front above the ear, to the temple and terminates at the external corner of the eyebrow. From the mastoid acupoint, a short internal branch, links the tragus (the small fleshy point directly in front of the ear opening), then to the tongue and joins the last surface point which is the start of the next meridian (gall bladder).

The Organ of the Triple Warmer – Function

The Triple Warmer gathers and regulates the Ki energy of the respiratory, digestive and sexual functions working in close cooperation with the organs of:

1. Lungs
2. Small intestine (absorption)
3. Kidneys (sex) + Circulation/Sex and Heart organ/function.

The Triple Warmer extracts and musters the energy from:

1. The burning of oxygen
2. Change of food into calories
3. The sexual fire

These three heat or cold generation "warmers" effectively control the temperature of the body, maintaining warmth in winter and keeping the body cool and comfortable in physical exertion and hot weather.

Danger Signals.

Inability to warm up or cool down when the weather changes: automatically wanting to turn on the house heater: oppressed by outdoor heat in country or natural surroundings: icy limbs, "frozen" arms and legs: cannot fold or stretch elbows: backbone pains in the heart region: cannot twist the chest or painful when turning: fever without perspiration: sudden acute heart pain, as if "Stunned by the Devil": epilepsy with vomiting of phlegm: moaning, fear, rambling thoughts and fantastic dreams: pain in gums and teeth: all teeth feel tight: pain in the cheek: swollen cheeks: swelling in throat: suddenly dumb - cannot speak -; dry mouth; no saliva; no appetite (should not eat); buzzing and pain in ears; unclear hearing; mastoiditis; sudden deafness and red inflamed eyes (especially painful at the external corner of eyes).

First Aid Acupoints

"Empty" vomiting, throat infection, dry mouth, loose tongue, cannot speak, loss of appetite, cholera . . . treat Tw 1

Migrane, headache, dizziness, deafness, eye infection . . .
. . . treat Tw 5

Duodenal ulcers, constipation, flu, middle ear infection . . .
. . . treat Tw 6/7

Internal parasites . . . . treat Tw 8

Shoulder rheumatism, eye inflammation, lift arm to treat . . .
. . . treat Tw 11

(deep and prolonged pressure permitted)

Epilepsy; sore shoulder blades; neck (cervical); lymph glands and nodes inflamed; "heavy" shoulders . . .
. . . treat Tw 12, 13 and 14

Middle ear and Eustachian canal inflamed, buzzing ears, convulsions, epilepsy with vomiting of phlegm, fever, nosebleed . . .
. . . treat Tw 18 to Tw 21

Upturned eyes (sanpaku); does not recognize anyone, dizzy, eyelashes curled inward; white veil on eyes; convulsions . . .
. . . treat Tw 23

Note: Forcibly suppressing anger leads to chronic tenseness in arms and all joints.

The Triple Warmer

Causes of Malfunction

It is the organic function of the Triple Warmer which atrophies and disappears first when man stops living naturally. Prior to that time, any change in the ambiant temperature, even extremes of cold and heat, are easily compensated by an immediate marshalling of the inner fire.

Cold felt on the skin and relayed to the parasympathetic nervous system will trigger an automatic lighting of one, two or even three internal furnaces:

1. Burning more oxygen in the lungs, often even without increasing the breath rhythm or capacity.

2. Metabolizing more food into calories.*

3. Arousing the sexual instinct is a powerful generator of Fire,**restoring Ki flow and producing overall warmth.

*If Triple Warmer no longer works, eating some food will generate heat but hot drinks will tax the kidney and bladder plus place an extra burden on the water-eliminating function of the intestine, creating MORE of a drain on this second warmer.

**When the sexual organs and the sexual response have been damaged, body warmth can only be generated by a willful increase of air or food intake or by the use of an external source of artificial heat. In addition to the causes of malfunction of the Triple Warmer, we must also consider all drugs having an influence on the parasympathetic nervous system, the various organs, the body metabolism and last but not least, living in an ever increasing alienation of the natural order -- in houses, cars, windowless factories, behind glass windows, cooled by artificial refrigeration with its extremes of cold and all of the technological systems of heating, air humidifiers, ionizers, etc . . .

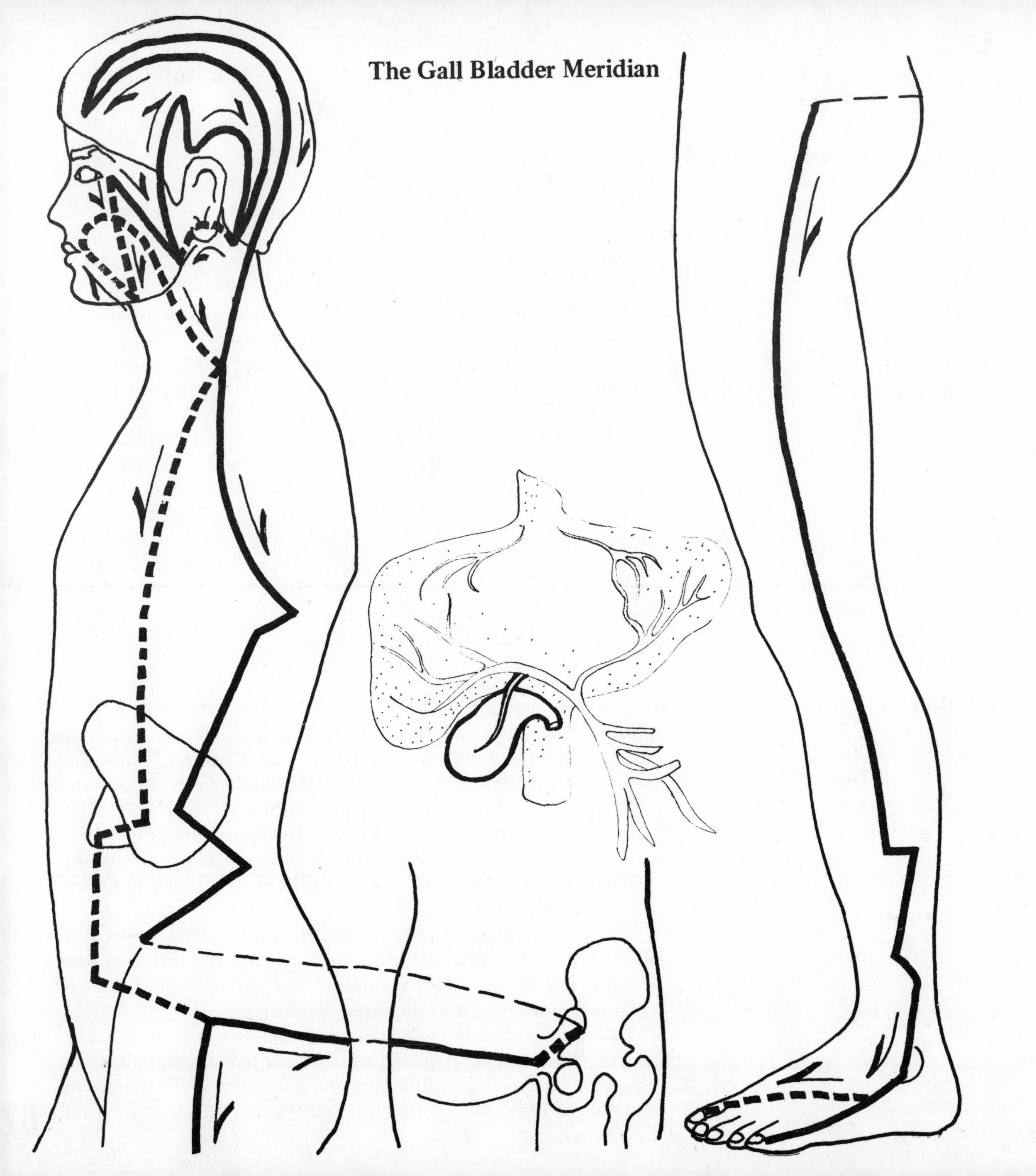
The Gall Bladder Meridian

Meridian Pathway

Starts at the external corner of the eye, down to the corner of the jaw hinge, up to the temple, contours the ear toward the rear then to the bottom rear of the cranial box. The meridian then returns to the front under the knob of the forehead, then again over to the back of the head and down to the scapular point of the cervical sympathetic ganglion. An internal link begins at the base of the skull, coursing through the inner ear to connect with a point in front of the external ear. A second internal link begins at the eye corner and courses through the jawbone, rising up through the eye orbit then descends to the collarbone to join with the surface point. From this point, Gb 21, two branches lead: One, in surface, descends to the side of the thorax and the belly, then to the waist and the lower buttocks, contouring to the front of the hip, it follows the outside part of the leg down to the foot to end at the angle of the nail of the 4th toe. A second link, internal, begins at the collarbone acupoint Gb 21, linking the liver and the gall bladder to join in surface at the point on the hip Gb 30, From the rear of the foot, the meridian has a short link branching out to the big toe, the first point of the liver meridian.

The Gall Bladder – The Organ

The gall bladder organ stores and concentrates a working fluid for digestion and elimination. This fluid called the bile is normally released only during the time of digestion. It has the ability of dissolving free fatty acids, cholesterol and lecithin. The color of the bile comes from two pigments (BILIRUBIN and UROBILIN). Bile which pours into chyme (digesting food) in the small intestine, not only helps digest and absorb fats but prevents intestinal putrefaction, contributes to peristaltic action and the voiding of the feces.

When fecal matter loses its brown red coloring - becomes white - it is due to the pigments by-passing the intestine and loading the blood, causing jaundice (yellow eyes and skin) -- cholemia -- or going into the urine (choluria).

Liver, spleen and the gall bladder cooperate in the production of bile. When the duct of the gall bladder to the small intestine closes or the organs malfunction, the bile changes in its concentration, its direction of flow or its amount released – then illness begins.

Malfunction

The following causes will contribute to the malfunction of the gall bladder organ: Overeating; diet of animal products and cholesterol (fats), refined sugar, refined grain products and spices, all vitamin pills and supplements, drugs; poor chewing; and lack of physical activity. Recommended: No more than 2 tablespoons of vegetable (unrefined quality) oil per day; unrefined sea salt, Tamari soy sauce only for condiments.

First Aid Acupoints

Poor eyesight: cannot see in the light of day (hemeralopia); dazzled by bright light; insists on wearing sun glasses; itching of eyes with headaches and migraines, eyes inflamed beginning at the external corner, abundant discharge of eye mucus . . . . . . treat Gb 1

Facial paralysis; crooked mouth and eyes; apoplexy (blockage of a blood vessel causing loss of bodily function) followed by paralysis of the four members; constant sadness; madness - the person runs constantly. Bad gums and loose teeth; swollen cheeks; jaws contracted preventing chewing; afraid of cold and wind; even cold food and water; uncontrolled foaming at the mouth . . . . treat Gb 2

Headaches, buzzing in ear; epilepsy, eye trouble; dizzy . . . . . . treat Gb 7/8/9/14

Bronchitis, asthma, spasm in the windpipe, tonsilitis; anemia; uremia; nose; ear and eye infections . . . treat Gb 20

Respiratory diseases; acute bile duct inflammation, liver ailment; acute kidney infection; hypertension . . . treat Gb 24/25

Constipation, infection of the genitals, inflamed testicles, inflamed uterus . . . . treat Gb 27

Low level of activity (lowering of the basal metabolism); water retention; illness of the intestines and of the bile ducts; constipation; jaundice . . . . treat Gb 34

Female reproductive organ infection (especially excess discharge) . . . . treat Gb 34

Enlarged heart; pain in heart; stiff tongue with dry mouth; sudden deafness; pain at the corner of the eyes; hard of breathing with fullness of chest; very hot palms and feet without perspiration . . . . treat Gb 44

Danger Signals

When the face color becomes "dusty", wan or livid and the skin is without luster; when there is bitterness in the mouth and pain is felt directly under the liver, at the sides and in the heart, preventing the patient from twisting around; and when the feet are warm, then the gall bladder is not in harmony and illness is about to set in.

When the illness has become established, there is intermittent fever with chills; the body perspires profusely; there is pain at the external corners of the eyes, at the side of the head a "tight band" feeling around the head and the chin; the armpits become swollen; and there is pain at the hip, the knee and finally at all of the articulations. It is then necessary to calm the energy of the small intestine.

Danger Signals

Liver illness is about to start in the organism when: There is constant dryness in the throat; acute pain in the liver area with inability to bend forward or backward, the color of the facial skin is weak and dirty. In man, small hernias appear in the genial, in women, there is swelling of the lower abdomen and pelvis.

The more advanced stage of the liver disease shows oppression and fullness in the chest, vomiting and diarrhea, stoppage of urination and defecation.

The Function of The the Liver

The liver is a versatile and multi-function organ which manufactures:

BILE To facilitate digestion and absorption of fats and help to contract the intestine for proper elimination. The liver also stores the bile (see gall bladder organ).

GLYCOGEN To transform sugars into glycogen and further change the latter into glucose, holding these substances in reserve for the body's changing requirements.

UREA This slightly toxic simple substance is used for the elimination of albuminoid waste.

In addition, the liver:

GUARDS As guardian of the non-toxic state of the body, the liver destroys and eliminates minerals, organic and medicinal toxins as well as infectious germs. This organ also detoxifies cellular waste matter and spent red blood cells, changing the hemoglobin into BILIRUBIN and BILIVERDIN, both colored matters found in the liver.

METABOLIZES FATS Under normal conditions and in the healthy organism, the liver transforms fats. When these are present in excess, the liver is able to destroy and eliminate the surplus.

Malfunction of the liver, in the presence of an excess of fats, loads the hepatic cell and enlarges the liver into adipose oversize organic tissues (enlarged liver).

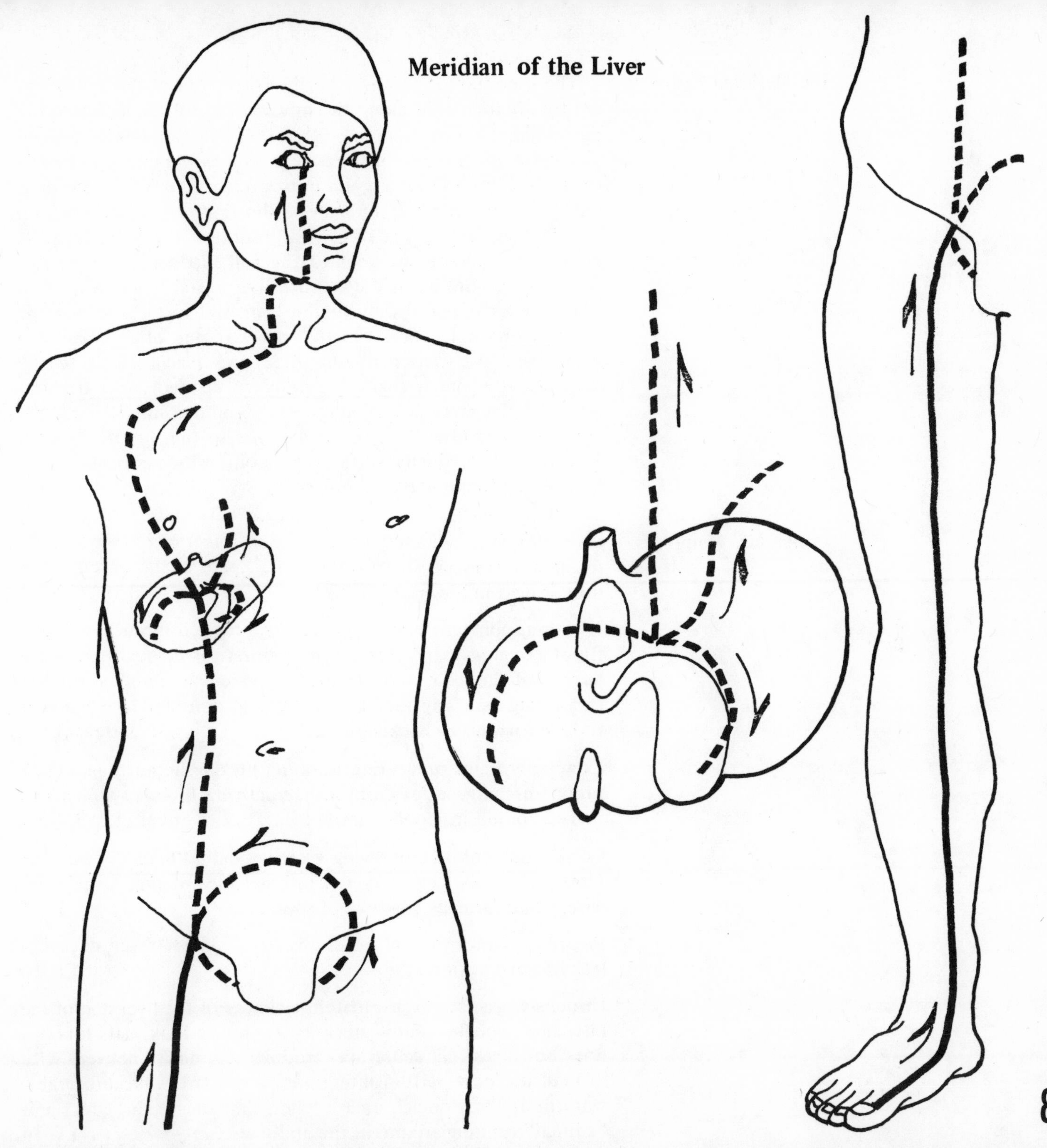
Meridian of the Liver

The Meridian Pathway

The meridian of the liver begins at the root of the nail of the big toe, it then rises along the internal face of the leg up to the pubic hair area at the femoral artery. The meridian internally surrounds the external genitals -- as well in man as in woman -- from there, still internally, it courses to the liver where the meridian divides into four branches: The first one remains within the liver and emerges at its lowest point near the 11th rib, at its point. The second one goes to the gall bladder and later surfaces on the thorax in the seventh intercostal space. The third branch rises internally above the liver and surfaces within the sixth intercostal space. Finally, the last one of the branches rises from the center of the liver and reaches first to the shoulder -- where it surfaces briefly to connect with the first point of the meridian of lungs, thus completing the circuit -- courses internally along the collarbone to the throat, the chin and the eyes to finally surface at a point which corresponds to the Bng 20 (brain nerve governor).

First Aid Acupoints

Liver illnesses, diabetes, gout, ovarian infections, infections of the penis, enuresis (bed wetting) . . . pain at the navel, sensation of heat in lower abdomen . . . . . . treat Lf 1

Hysteria, constant anger, sighs a lot, crooked mouth, epilepsy, fit of coughing, dry throat, great thirst, atrocious pain at the heart and the liver, accompanied by greenish complexion "like in a dying man", swollen knees, icy cold arms and legs, inability to lean forward or backward . . . . . . treat Lf 2

Low belly pains preventing walking, uterine hemorrhage, black blood discharge after childbirth, vomiting blood; swollen lips, nausea, blood in stools, diarrhea . . . . . . treat Lf 3/4/5/6

Colic, tuberculosis following excesses and "binges", pus and blood in stools, aches on the internal face of thighs, liver disease, vulvar pruritis, absence of sperm . . . . . . Lf 8

Pleurisy, cannot urinate, insomnia or sleepiness, fever, excess or lack of perspiration . . . . . . Lf 10

Dispepsia, gas, stomach bloated, sickness of the liver and of the bile duct, cough, yellow-green face, skinny look, eats lots but does not digest, all acute liver troubles, childbirth delivery with difficulties, post partum infections, very hard belly, unbearable warmth at the stomach area in chest and the feeling of a small "animal" running around in the abdomen . . . . . . Lf 14

Rheumatism

Ancient medicine offers simple and effective treatment for this painful ailment. Traditional healing recognized long ago that three external and aggressive elements were partly responsible for rheumatism when coupled with a lowered resistance of the body which allowed them to perform their breakdown action. Internal predisposition made an unbalanced organism receptive to the illness.

One of the defensive functions of the meridian system and of Ki flow is to shield the body against disrupting external agents. This guardian role is under the form of thermal and vasomotor actions (nerves regulating the diameter of the blood vessels in the threatened areas) and in the reaction of perspiration.

The illness itself is very ancient and under the Ming dynasty was said to be caused by "Lessening of the energy caused by a lack of biological discipline which weakened the internal fortitude and a lack of tonicity". Wu Wei-P'ing cited the internal predisposition of the weakened, the saddened, the unsatisfied, the unfulfilled, the chronically fatigued, and those who habitually partake of sweet or alcoholic beverages. It is by the energy disruption of the organism that the tissues and the joints are made vulnerable. So much for the original cause.

Now for the triggering mechanisms -- sudden changes in climate or atmospheric condition, simple exposure to rain or wind, residence in humid climate, poorly adapted clothing for the season, exposure to sudden cooling in the midst of great heat (such as the air-conditioned home, car or office) or exposure to a draft during sleep when the physical energy is in repose. These always invite the outside negative destructive energy which overpowers the weakened defense mechanism of the body.

In rheumatism:

Wind	is responsible for disruption of functions and organs.
Cold	is to be blamed for pains due to circulatory slowdown.
Dampness	is the cause of secretion and humors.

Relief of pain and symptoms

The success of the treatment has been proven and has been classified by body regions:

Localized:	Shoulders	Bv 11, Sig 12 and Lig 15
	Arms (Upper)	Lig 14
	Elbows	Lig 11 and Lp 5
	Forearms	Lig
	Hips	Gvb [illegible]
	Thighs	Gvb 31
	Knees	Gvb 34, Bv 53, Se 34 and 35
	Legs	Bv 57, Sp 6
	Back	Bng 9, Bng 13
	Lumbar region	Bv 25, Bv 47
In the case of non-localized pains - Erratic zones		Lig 11 and Bv 54

For all of the above regions and specific pressure points, the initial treatment must consist of a slow and prolonged deep massage in the direction of the meridian flow underlying the pressure point being treated. This will act to cancel and expel the external destructive energy. Points indicated must be treated, on both sides of the body and for a duration of 20 minutes each. Rest and limited exercises plus fasting is required for the next 48 hours. Bancha tea with Tamari Soy sauce - maximum 300 cc. (10 fluid ounces) per day. Follow with a second treatment of the same points 48 hours after the first, but with light, rapid and brief finger pressure in order to strengthen the energetic immune (defense) system of the meridian involved.

In the case of swolleness or distention at the specific points indicated for treatment, do not treat those points but instead use deep sustained and prolonged finger massage on the nearest points on the meridian cited in the table. When the swelling has subsided, resume the treatment as indicated in the previous paragraph.

Rheumatoid Arthritis

For rheumatoid arthritis, each articulation affected must be treated with moxabustion using mugwort until the skin reddens and deep perspiration occurs.

Further Treatment for Rheumatism

The unbalance of the energy which is the real cause of the vulnerability of the body to the climatic attacks; now requires attention, otherwise within a short time, a relapse will occur. The suprarenal cortex and the kidneys secrete insufficiently -- Yin -- and require inductive stimulation through Do-in breathing exercises as well as improvement in the diet, drink and food habits. A specific remedy for the stimulation of the kidneys is a tea made of small deep red "aduki" beans.

The Western medicine treats the organism with doses of ACTH and corticol hormones, however, as more drugs are supplied, the more the organism relies on this outside help and the less it will supply these hormones on its own. Thus, an invalid has been created whose "improved" condition is wholly dependant on an artificial glandular treatment. Laboratory tests have proven that frequent stimulation of a single point "Bv 23" by percussion, self-massage or even less frequently moxabustion were sufficient to reestablish the natural secretions of the 11 oxy-steroids.

How to Do the "Inner" Exercises

The scientific Western mind does not comprehend how internal organs can be influenced by the will alone, yet, the traditional physician versed in the ancient medical arts states emphatically that "inner" organs will be healed by Do-in.

In order to understand how inner organs are affected, we must remember first that each Do-in exercise breaks down into two cycles, and that each cycle moves the diaphragm by air: Inspiration and exhalation.

All Do-in exercises involve the control of the breath. If they are not so indicated, one's own intuition must be used to breathe out (discharge) at the propitious time. The rise and fall displacement of the diaphragm directly affects each internal organ. With adequate daily practice and concentration, the internal organ will benefit. As they gradually obey the command of the will, their optimum function will be restored.

Postscript

The Global Origin of Do-in

In 1966, the teaching of Dō-in in the U.S.A. stemmed from the efforts of one man, Mr. Michio Kushi, a Japanese scholar whose multitude of other courses and interests prevented him from disseminating this knowledge more fully.

Fired by the potential of this almost forgotten science, my growing awareness of its benefits to man and the urging of Mr. Kushi, moved me to publish a small booklet with 100 pictures called "The First Book of Dō-in". The publication date was June 1971.

Earlier, in 1968, some European students had asked that the book be made available in French as well as English. To comply with their wish, the bilingual edition was printed and soon reached much farther than France and England without any publicity save by word of mouth of the Voice of Nature. Foreign editions translated in other languages are now in progress in Spanish, Portuguese, German, Italian and Afrikaan.

Feedback from the wide dissemination of the Art of Dō-in shed much new light onto this discipline. Some Do-in books found their way into Africa, New Zealand, New South Wales, Korea, Ireland, etc . . . Also to Japan where Do-in has been practiced and taught orally for centuries. In China a form of Dō-in *Tao-yinn* - meaning "to lead with the breath" - used for the preservation of life (*yang-sheng*) is taught to patients in the hospitals for restorative purposes. (See chapter "Modern Clinical Dō-in in China").

A most fortunate encounter in August 1973 with Sensei Masaichi Enomoto – possibly the most knowledgeable teacher of Dō-in in Japan – allowed me to learn in private with a master. Many of his breathing exercises are incorporated in the present volume.

Modern Chinese clinics, Japanese scholars and foreign students added their valuable contribution to the store of knowledge inherited from my distant ancestors in Gaul and their Druid healers and to the early practices of the Persians, the Egyptians, the Essenes, the Hemerobaptists, the Ayurvedic and the Malay folk doctors. These additions brought changes in the manner of practicing the art of Dō-in as well as a much wider perspective on its link to the health sciences of the past.

The history of man's own efforts at maintaining health, his empirical remedies and self-cures, fascinate me more than cultural or general history. Ancient medical texts abound in accounts of the exploits and prowesses of famous physicians, huge compendiums of magical pharmaceutical herbs, Materia Medica, diagnosis and clinical records. But a charting of the practical and effective ways man has used for remaining healthy, happy and peaceful had never been compiled. The study of the metaphysics of health needed a compilation of the valid ancient method of self-healing for the regeneration of the body and soul of man by his own efforts.

But this was unexplored territory especially when the study of self-healing broadened to countries outside the Orient and the Americas. The words of Einstein: "Imagination is more important than Knowledge" as well as my intuition sustained my faith. Imagination and my own experience have been used when omissions or outright errors were found in transposed ancient writings.

Heinz Mode, the German Archeologist once wrote that faulty judgement has more worth than interminable waiting and that ancient history is continuously being disproved by new findings. Future revisions of this book of Dō-in will gratefully include criticisms and contributions by experts, researchers and men of good judgement. In advance, I wish here to welcome their patient cooperation; their suggestions are essential if present errors and omissions are to be corrected, their labors will be truly appreciated.

To the Voice of Nature and the many people who contributed so generously to the present book, to all those who made this second Book of Dō-in possible, my deepest gratitude. Their travail will be rewarded by many successful healings in other mortals through a deeper recognition of the "almost stilled" Voice of Nature.

Magalia Winter Solstice 1974

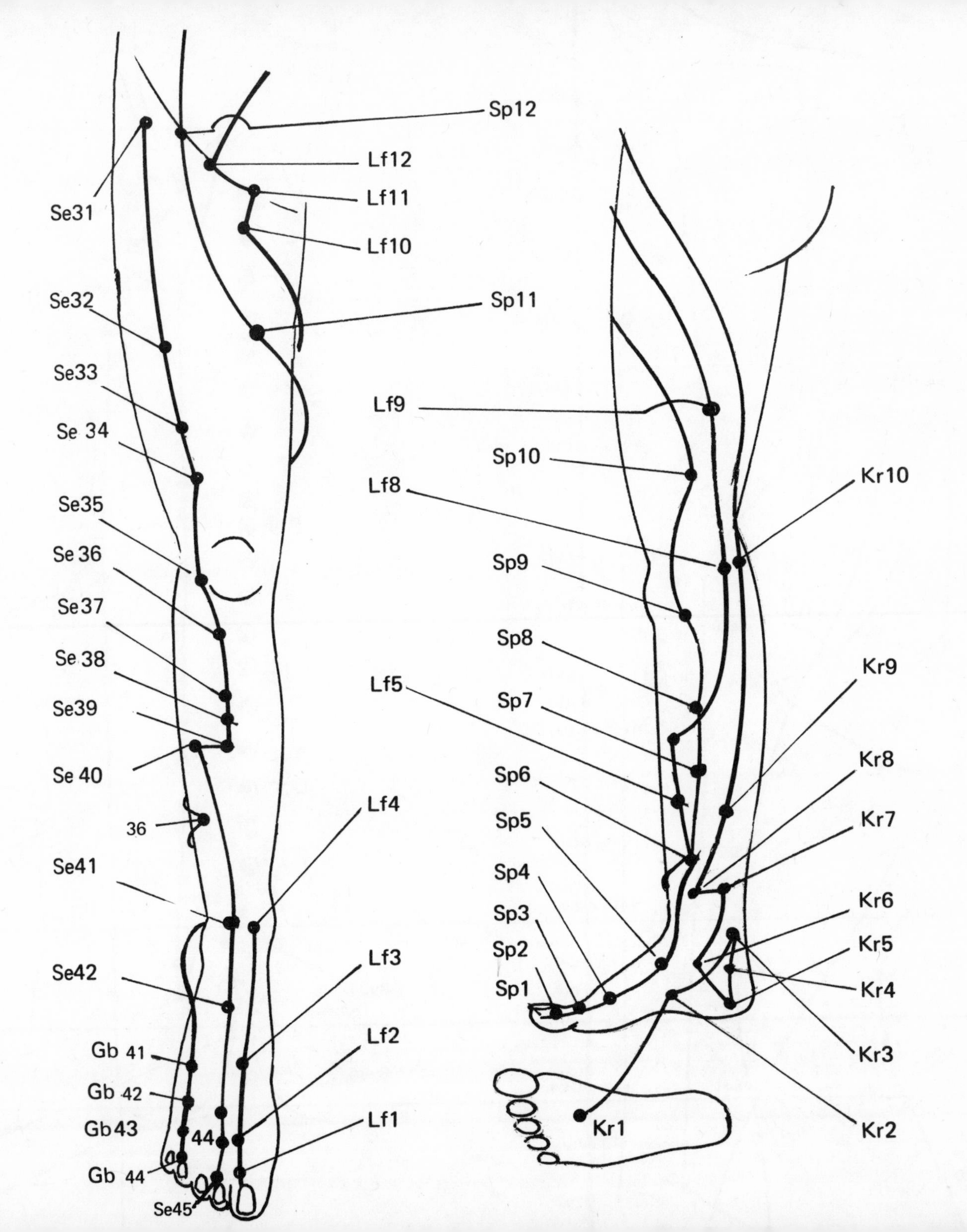
Sp12
Lf12
Se31
Lf11
Lf10
Se32
Sp11
Se33
Lf9
Se 34
Sp10
Kr10
Lf8
Se35
Se 36
Sp9
Se37
Sp8
Se 38
Kr9
Lf5
Sp7
Se39
Kr8
Se 40
Sp6
Lf4
Kr7
Sp5
36
Se41
Sp4
Kr6
Sp3
Kr5
Sp2
Se42
Lf3
Sp1
Kr4
Lf2
Gb 41
Kr3
Gb 42
Gb43
Lf1
44
Kr1
Kr2
Gb 44
Se45

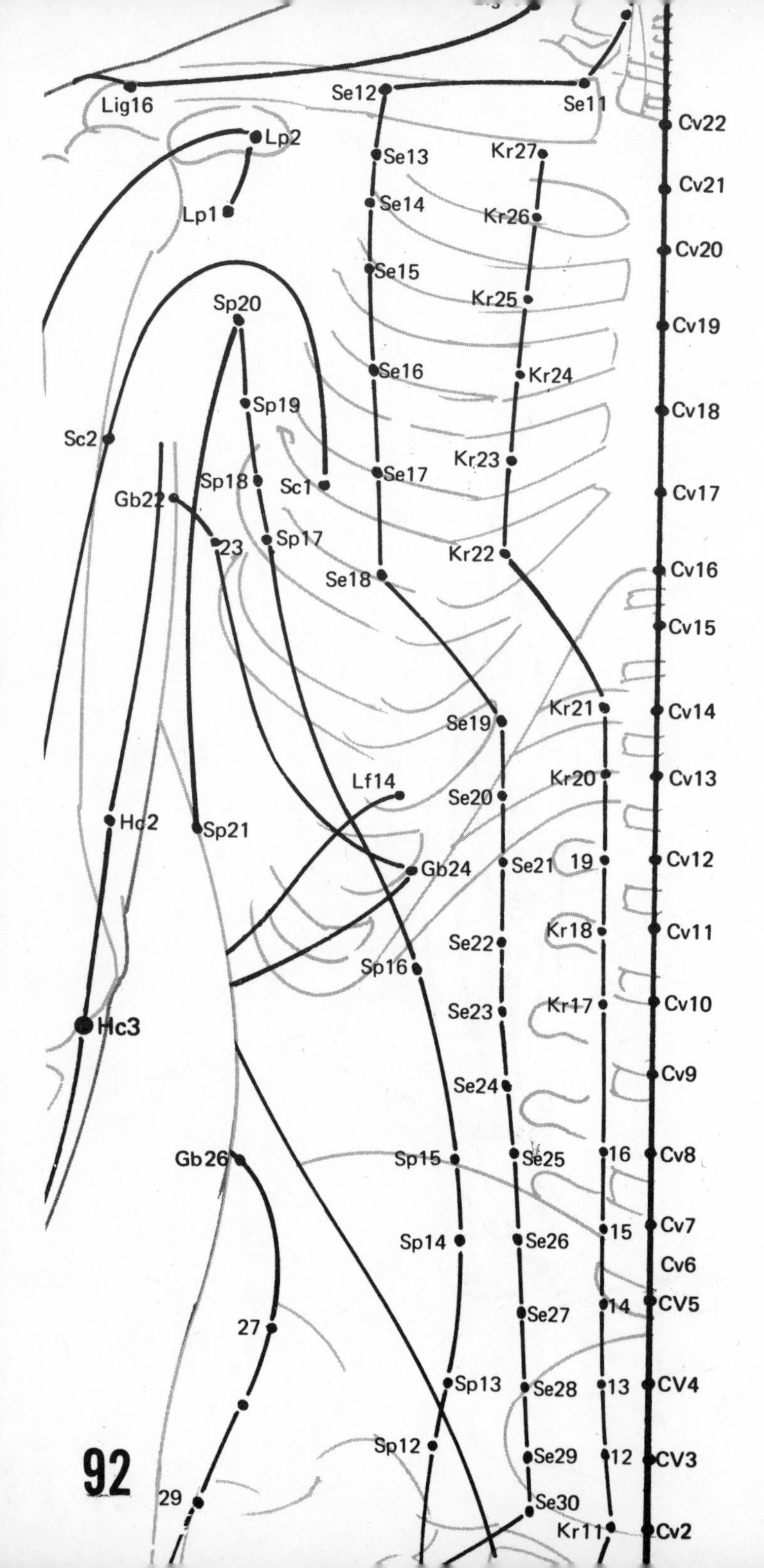

Lig16
Se12
Se11
Cv22
Lp2
Se13
Kr27
Cv21
Lp1
Se14
Kr26
Cv20
Se15
Kr25
Sp20
Cv19
Se16
Kr24
Sp19
Cv18
Sc2
Kr23
Se17
Sp18
Sc1
Cv17
Gb22
23
Sp17
Kr22
Se18
Cv16
Cv15
Kr21
Cv14
Se19
Lf14
Kr20
Cv13
Se20
Hc2
Sp21
Se21
19
Cv12
Gb24
Kr18
Cv11
Se22
Sp16
Kr17
Cv10
Se23
Hc3
Cv9
Se24
Gb26
Sp15
Se25
16
Cv8
Sp14
Se26
15
Cv7
Cv6
27
Se27
14
CV5
Sp13
Se28
13
CV4
Sp12
Se29
12
CV3
29
Se30
Kr11
Cv2

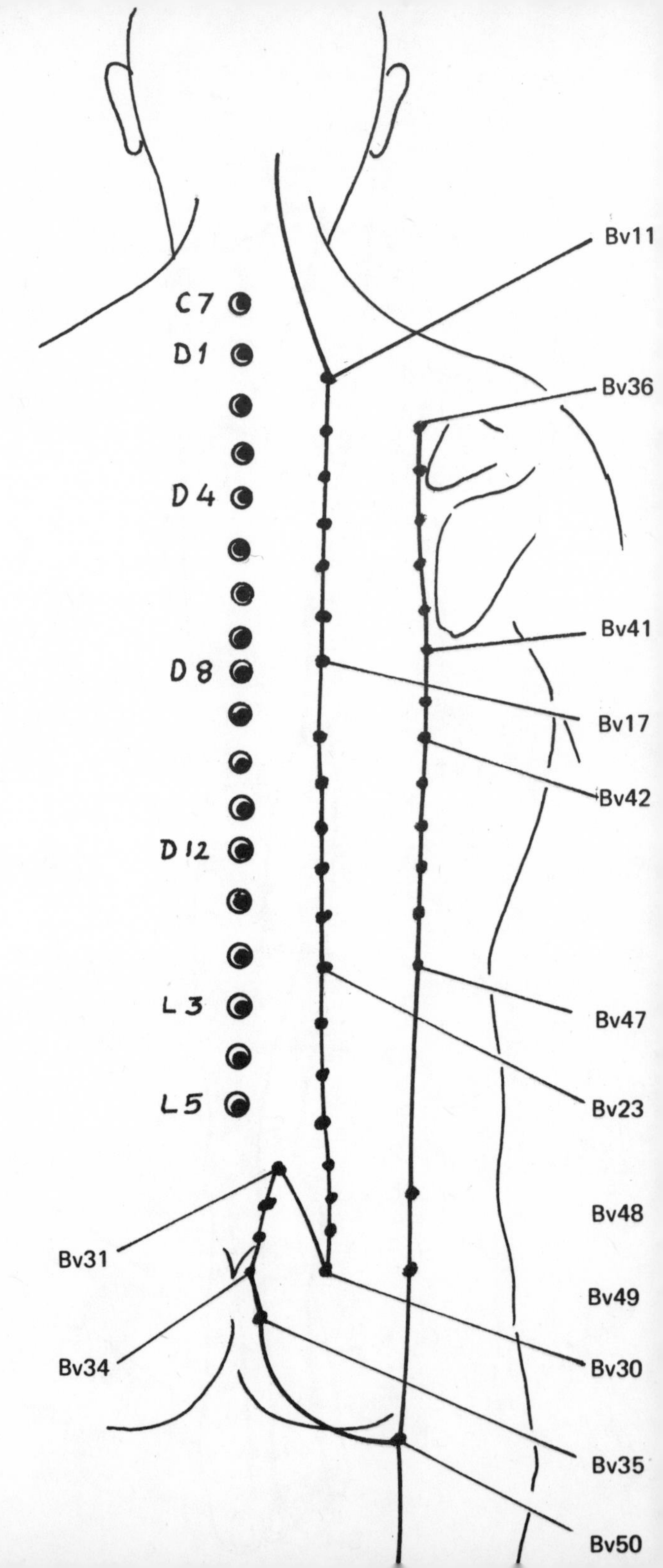

C7
D1
D4
D8
D12
L3
L5
Bv11
Bv36
Bv41
Bv17
Bv42
Bv47
Bv23
Bv48
Bv31
Bv49
Bv34
Bv30
Bv35
Bv50

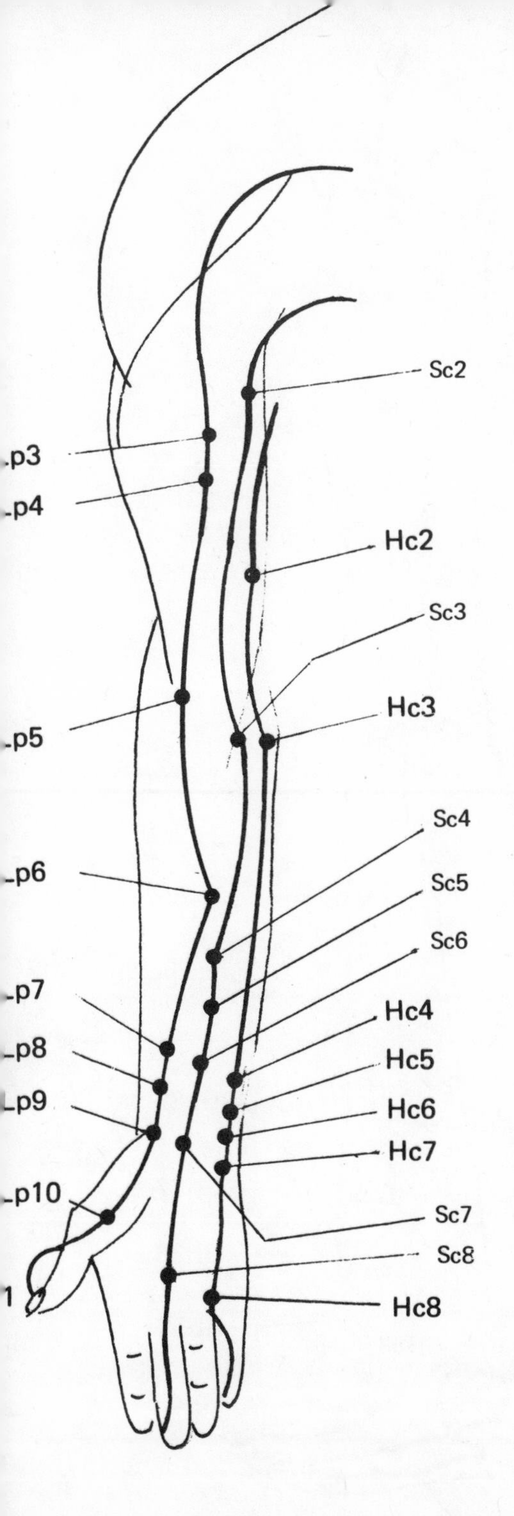
p3
p4
Hc2
Sc2
Sc3
p5
Hc3
p6
Sc4
Sc5
Sc6
p7
Hc4
p8
Hc5
Lp9
Hc6
Hc7
p10
Sc7
Sc8
1
Hc8

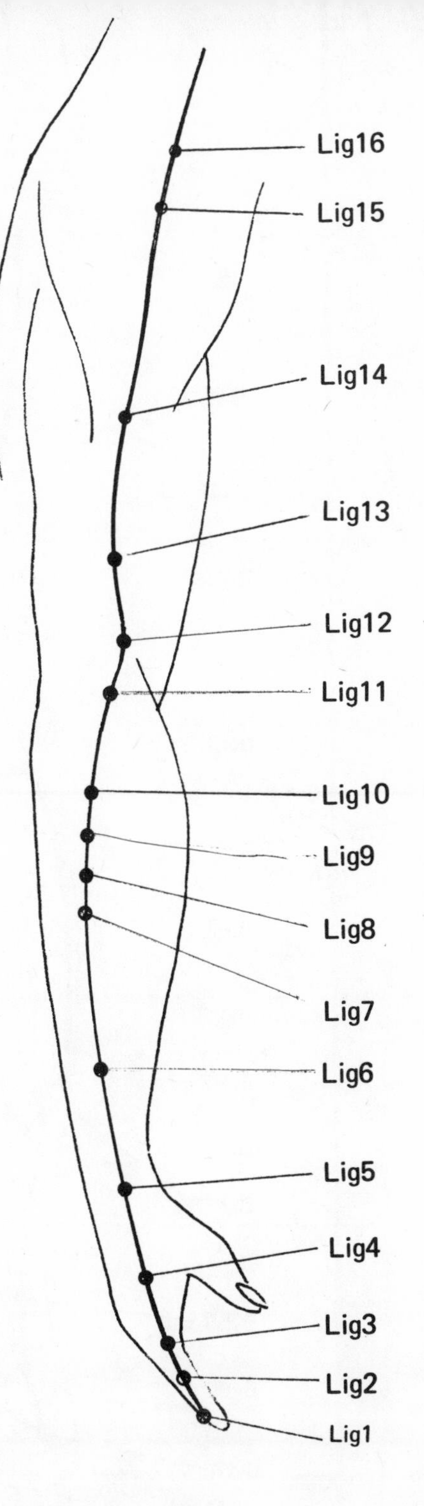
Lig16
Lig15
Lig14
Lig13
Lig12
Lig11
Lig10
Lig9
Lig8
Lig7
Lig6
Lig5
Lig4
Lig3
Lig2
Lig1

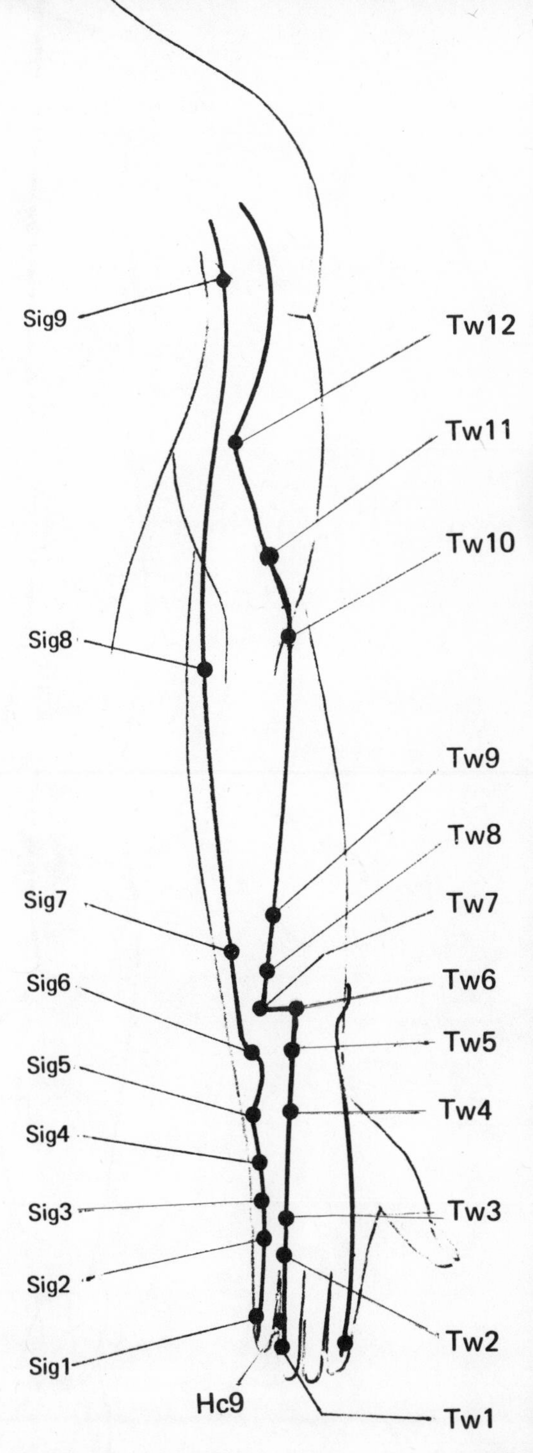
Sig9
Tw12
Tw11
Tw10
Sig8
Tw9
Tw8
Sig7
Tw7
Sig6
Tw6
Tw5
Sig5
Tw4
Sig4
Sig3
Tw3
Sig2
Tw2
Sig1
Hc9
Tw1

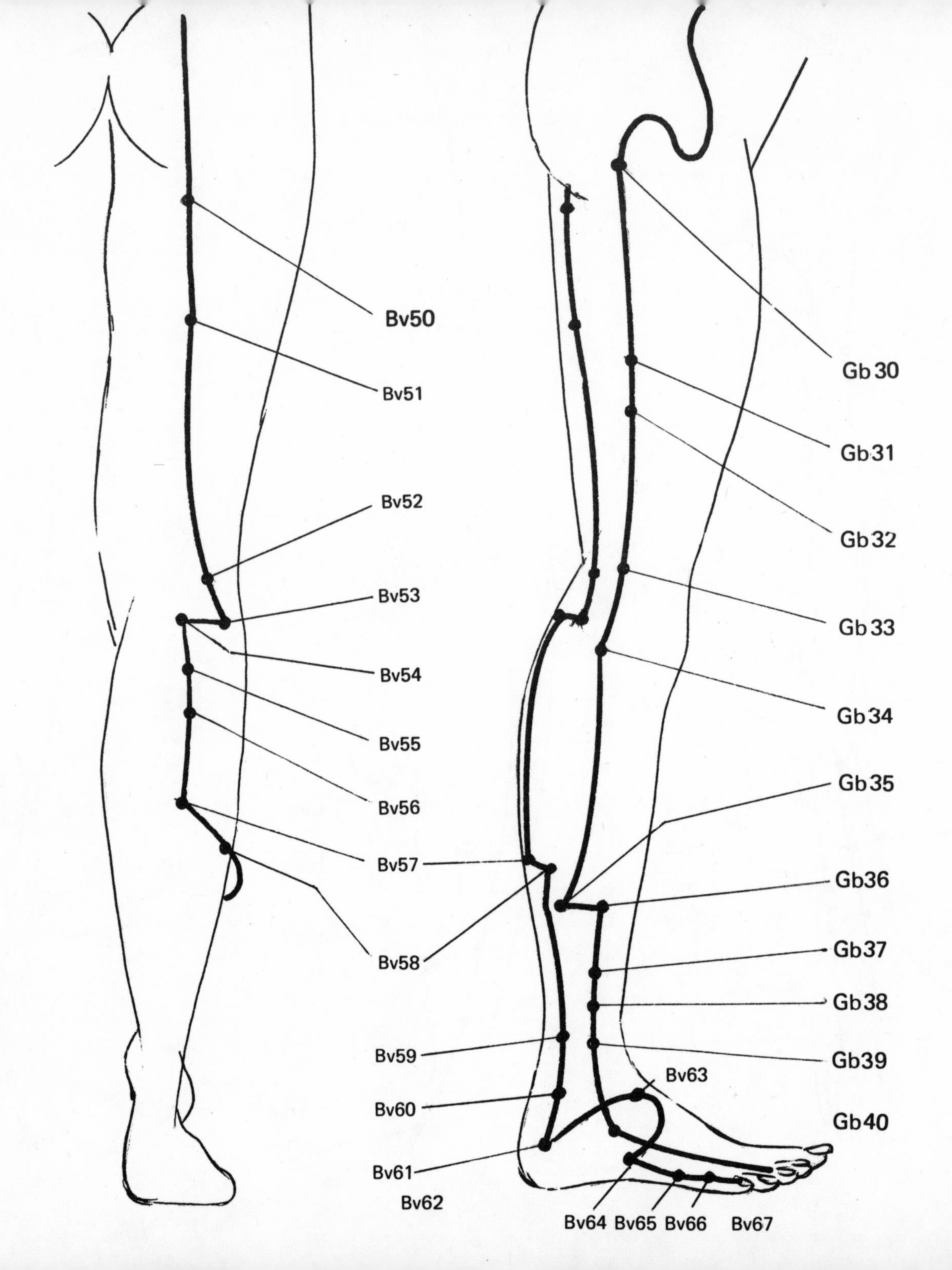
Bv50
Bv51
Bv52
Bv53
Bv54
Bv55
Bv56
Bv57
Bv58
Bv59
Bv60
Bv61
Bv62
Gb30
Gb31
Gb32
Gb33
Gb34
Gb35
Gb36
Gb37
Gb38
Gb39
Gb40
Bv63
Bv64
Bv65
Bv66
Bv67

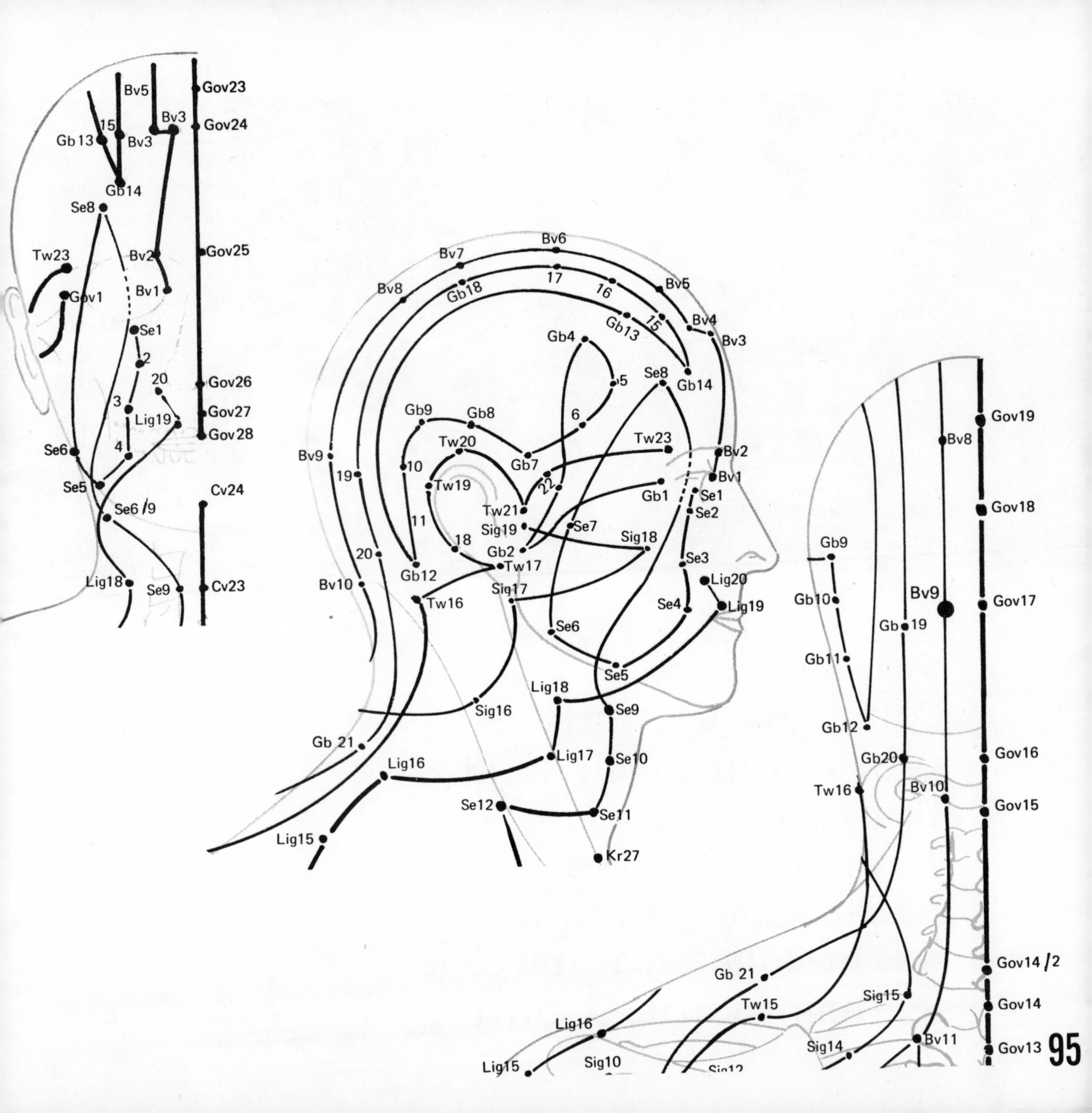

Bv5
Gov23
Bv3
Gov24
15
Gb 13
Bv3
Gb14
Se8
Bv2
Gov25
Tw23
Gov1
Bv1
Se1
2
20
Gov26
3
Gov27
Lig19
Gov28
Se6
4
Se5
Cv24
Se6 /9
Lig18
Se9
Cv23
Bv6
Bv7
17
Bv8
Gb18
16
Bv5
Gb13
15
Bv4
Bv3
Gb4
Se8
5
Gb14
6
Gb9
Gb8
Tw23
Tw20
Bv2
Bv9
10
Gb7
19
22
Bv1
Tw19
Gb1
Se1
Tw21
Se2
11
Se7
Sig19
Sig18
18
20
Gb2
Tw17
Se3
Gb12
Lig20
Bv10
Sig17
Tw16
Se4
Lig19
Se6
Se5
Lig18
Se9
Sig16
Gb 21
Lig17
Se10
Lig16
Se12
Se11
Lig15
Kr27
Gov19
Bv8
Gov18
Gb9
Bv9
Gov17
Gb10
Gb 19
Gb11
Gb12
Gov16
Gb20
Tw16
Bv10
Gov15
Gov14 /2
Gb 21
Sig15
Gov14
Tw15
Lig16
Bv11
Sig14
Gov13
Lig15
Sig10

Sun, sun divine,
Come give to earth
your warmth, your light
that man awaits
In the sky as you pass,
resplendant, vermillion,
it is the night that you chase.
Return, return, O Sun.

Ancient Druid Incantation to the Sun
(translated from the french)

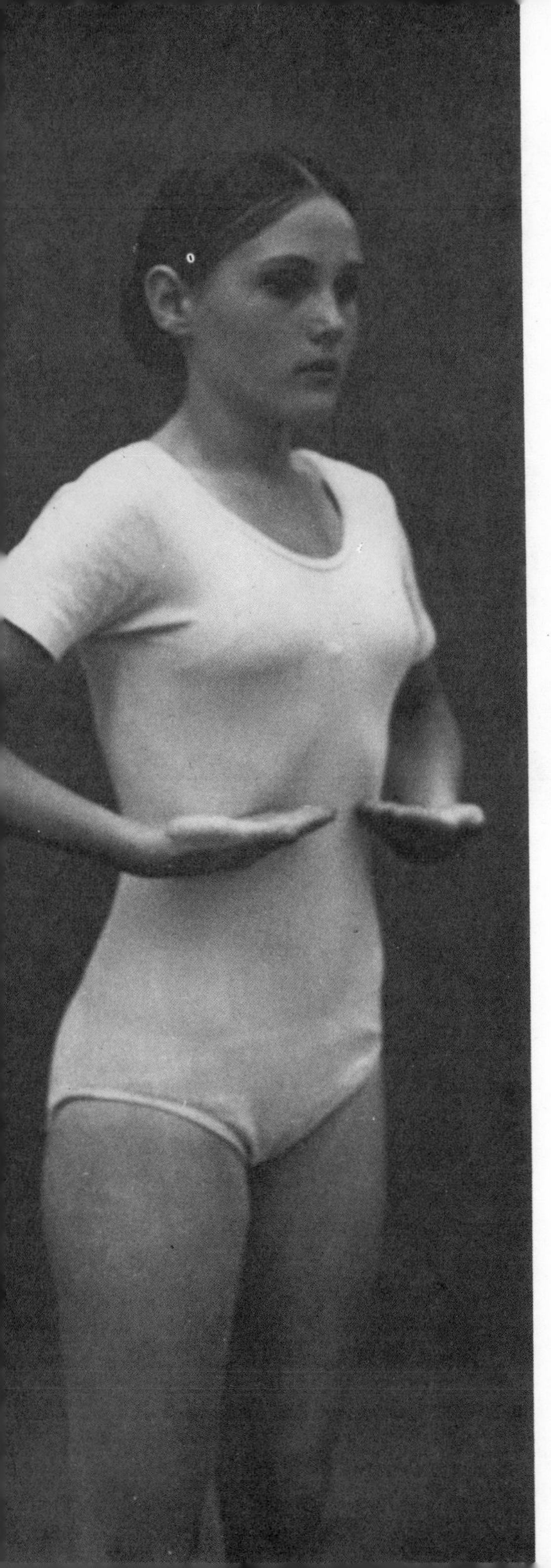

The Practice of Self healing

#1 The First Regenerative Breathing° Exercise...

At left:

Bring the hands up to ribcage, palms upward, breathe in through the nose, mouth is shut...INHALE

At right:

Stretch one arm up and turn the palm upward, look at the back of the hand EXHALE

Keep the other hand with the palm facing down and pulling downward hard.

Exercise #2

SALUTATION TO THE SUN

Best results are obtained when performed early in the morning, facing the rising sun. Standing.

Place the feet close together, big toes should be touching, inner ankle bones tightly wedged against each other.

EXHALE

Stretch both arms forward horizontally, fingers "wrapping" around the sun and enclosing the Ki that emanates from it,

INHALE

and pull both hands to the armpits (Lp 2), lung and breathing stimulation point.

At the same time, lift the heels alternatively and rub the ankle bones together, this stimulates (Kr 3 to Kr 5*) the kidneys

Repeat this breathing exercise with slow and deep (abdomen) breathing (7 times)

The above etching circa 1880 depicts a primitive man saluting the sun, Western man did not comprehend this practice

For an exact location of the points mentioned at left, please refer to the diagrams on pages 92 & 91

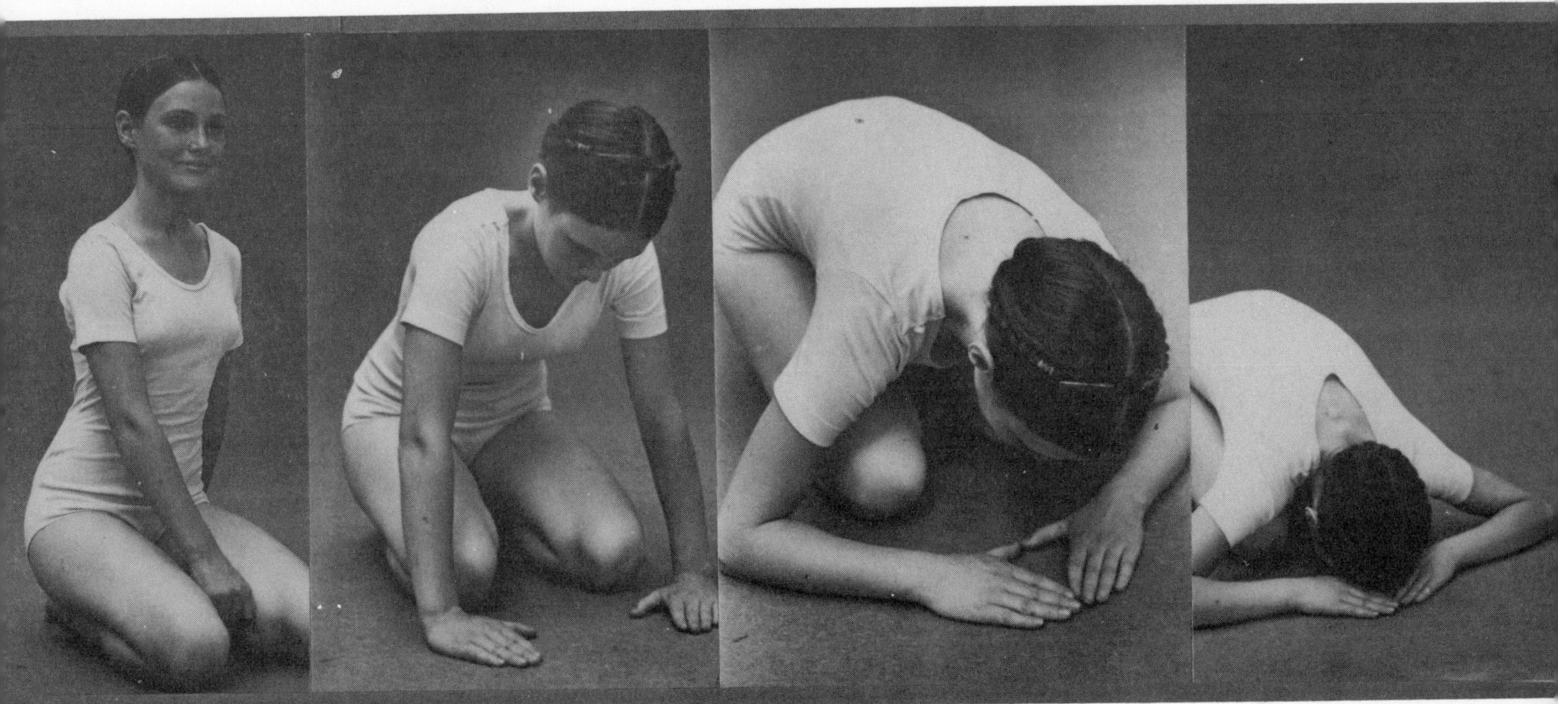

Exercise # 3
SEIZA - SALUTATION TO THE SUN

Sitting on heels, knees one fist apart
INHALE

Place hands flat on the ground on each side of
the thighs and slowly slide them forward while
bending the trunk EXHALE
and continue inclining the upper part of the
body until the chest touches the knees; the
hands are now forming a triangle (frame #3) into
which the forehead is placed, touching the ground,
when the lungs are completely empty, remain so for
a few moments and begin raising the trunk, INHALE
and complete the movement, returning slowly to the
first position shown at the left.

Exercise #4

THE SCISSORS

EXHALE

and compress the chest cavity by crossing both arms; slowly uncross and raise the arms above the shoulders and toward the rear while

INHALING

allow the air to remain in the lungs, mixing-in the breath

EXHALE

forcefully while quickly closing the arms and return to the first position shown at the left.

5 6

#5

GATHERING KI THROUGH THE FINGERTIPS

Rub the palms of the hands together while holding them above the eyes, continue until fingers become warm and the Ki flows.

To strengthen the heart, rub hard until perspiration gathers in the armpits.

#6

THE BIG EXPELLER

Cup the hands and rest them in the lap INHALE and begin lifting the buttocks from the heels, bring the air that is trapped within the hands forcefully into the lower abdomen, releasing the breath through the mouth at the same time, keep the belly soft, lean the trunk forward, repeat 7x

The ancient traditional medicine regarded this mixing-in the breath practice as superior.
See "Gas" page 53

7 8 9

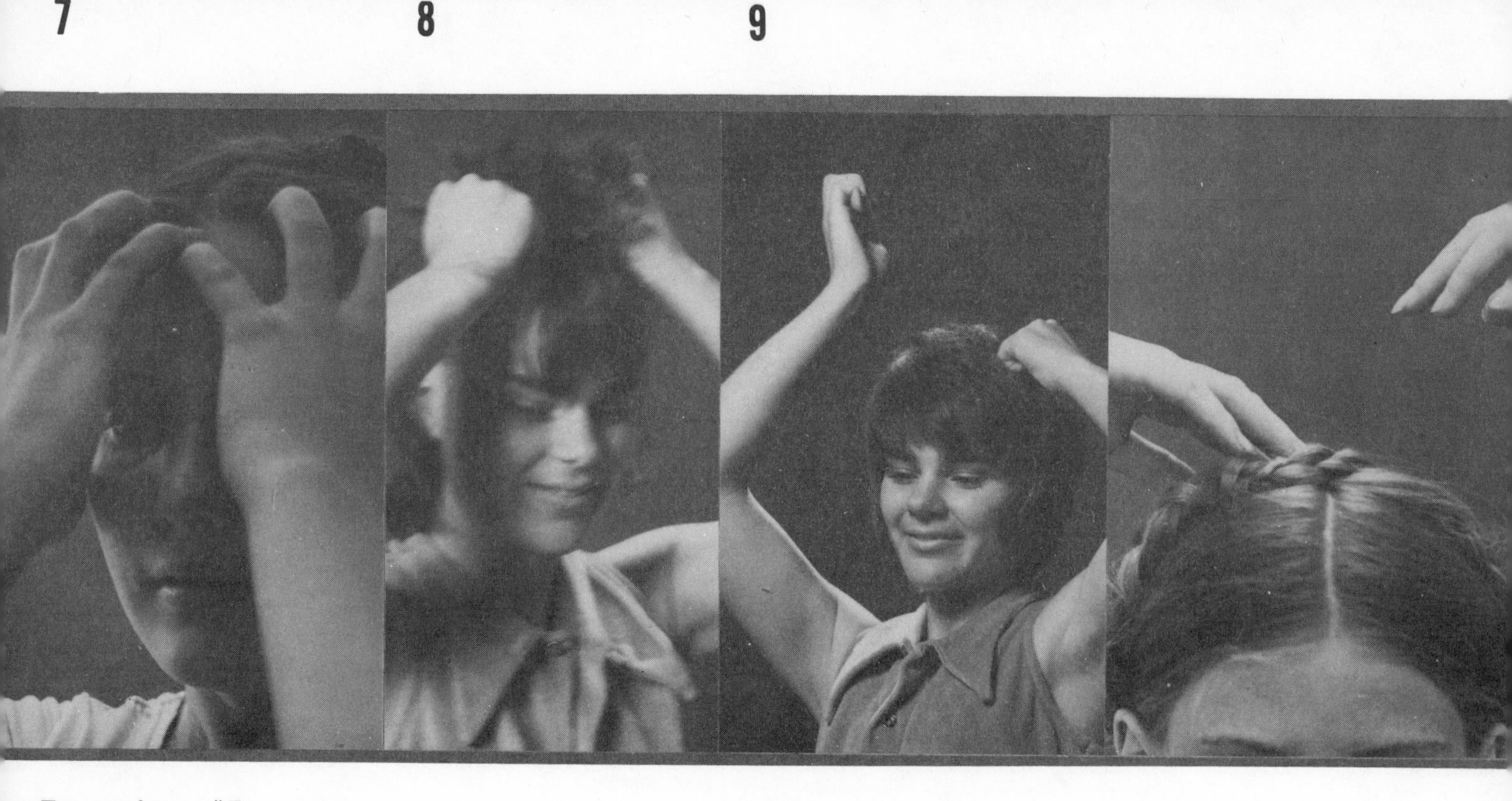

Exercise #7

Place all 8 fingers as shown "digging" into the hairline, move the forehead and the scalp up and down forcefully while taking in short breaths

Exercise #8
PULLING THE HAIR

Grab handfulls of hair and pull up, around and back and forth until the scalp tingle.

Exercise #9
DRUMMING ON THE HEAD

With flexible wrists, allow the knuckles or the fingertips to drop rhythmically on the top and on the side of the head, no "pounding" is required, only light drumming.

0 11 12

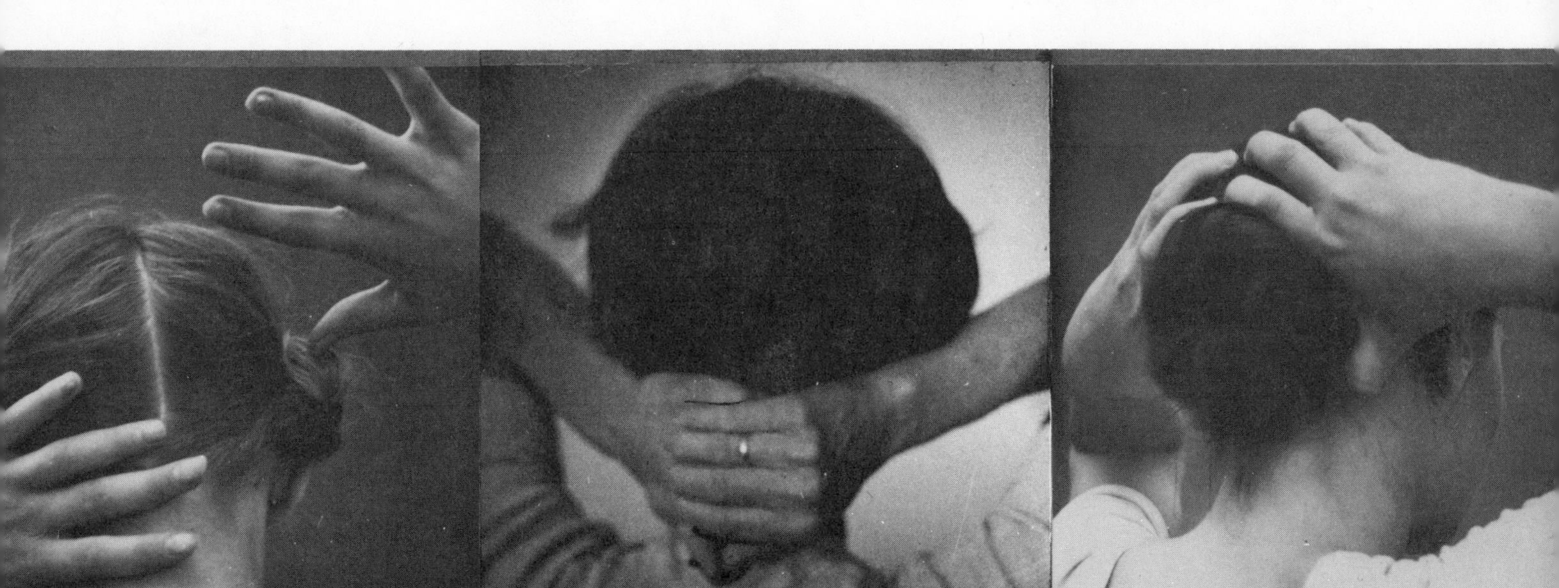

0 FANNING THE NECK

ing upward strokes,
th fingers extended,
b the entire back of
e neck, starting as
w as possible.

#11 PALMS AND FINGERTIPS ON THE NECK

Place one hand on top of the other and knead the muscles of the neck until softened. Repeat changing hands.

Stimulates Gov 12 to Gov 16 as well as Bladder and Gall Bladder meridians.

12 TRIPLE WARMER

With both hands on top of the head, massage with the tips of the thumb on Tw 16* then Gb 20 and Bv 10.

*See diagram, page 95

13 14

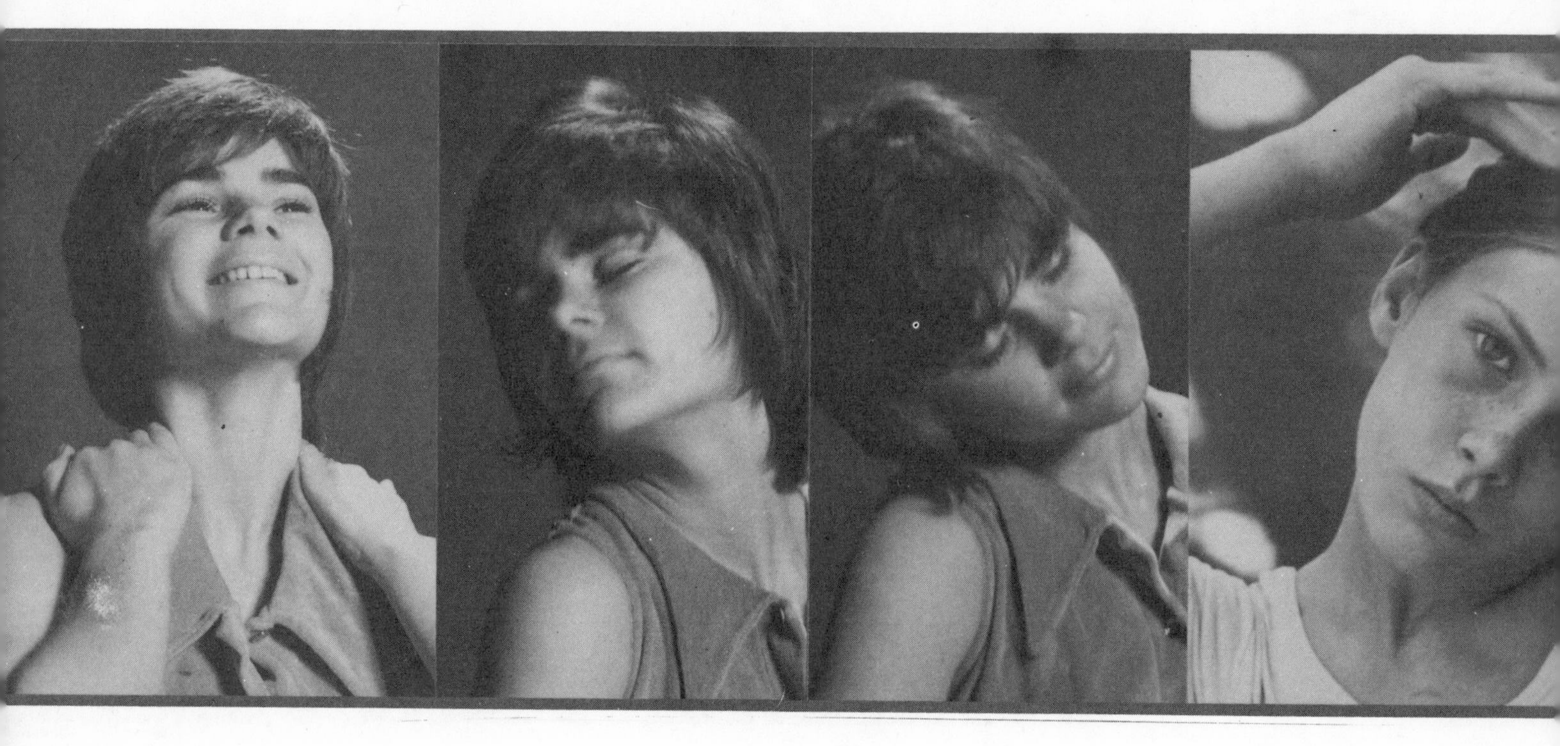

#14
#13

KNEADING THE SIDE
OF THE NECK

Using the heel of the hands and the finger-tips, squeeze and deep massage the flesh of the neck.
Lig 16 to 18
Gb 21 and Tw 15
are stimulated
(see Page 95 diagram)

#14
ROTATE THE HEAD

Make a full circle slowly, letting the head roll round

LOWER THE HEAD
SIDEWAYS

Drop the head sideways until the ear touches the shoulder, (do not raise the shoulder!) At the start, some gentle pushing with one hand will help but when there is pain or difficulty experienced in lowering the head, it indicates that the Triple Warmer lacks in Ki energy
(See page 78 to 80)

15 16 17

#15
INHALE and hold the breath, bend the head forward on the chest until chin touches it, open the mouth and allow the breath to escape forcefully

If pain is felt while doing the above head bend, it indicates a lack of energy in the liver (See page 85 and 86 for relief.)

#16
Place one hand on the chin and the other on top of the head INHALE twist the head sideways and look up, open the mouth and EXHALE force-fully.

#17
Same movement as on the left (#16) but head moves by itself without hands

When turning the head causes pain or becomes difficult, the small intestine is low in energy, so treats its meridian.

18 19 20

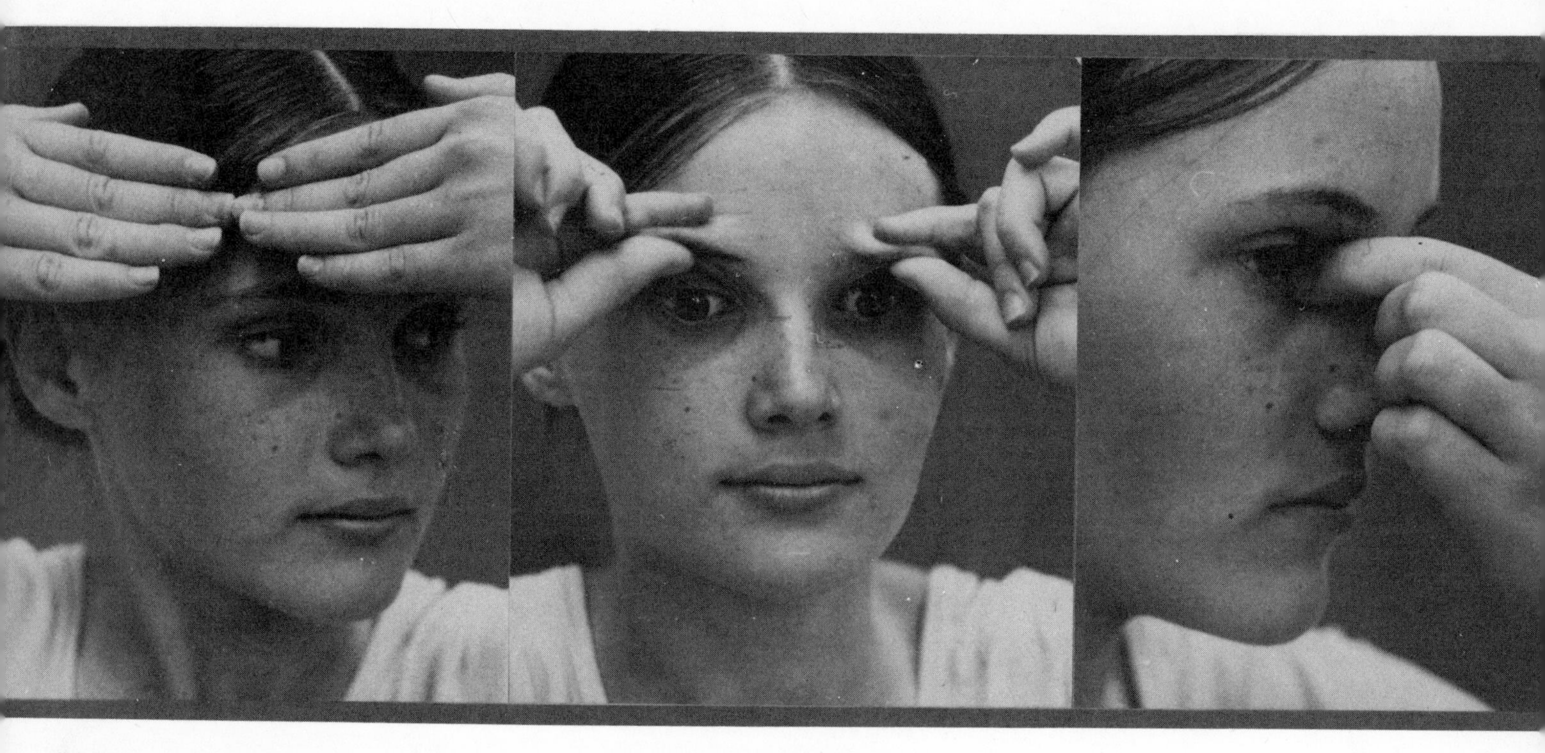

#18
With the fingers touching place strong hand pressure on the forehead, move the head back and forth.

Top line of forehead depicts the Circulatory System Middle line is for the Nervous System while Bottom line stands for the Digestive System

#19
PINCH THE EYEBROWS
Pinch and pull the fleshy part of the eyebrow, begin at the bridge of the nose and work to the outward corner of the eyes.

#20
With thumb and index finger push in and squeeze together in order to deeply massage the inner corners of the eye

At this point, the first acu- point of the Bladder is foun

21 22 23

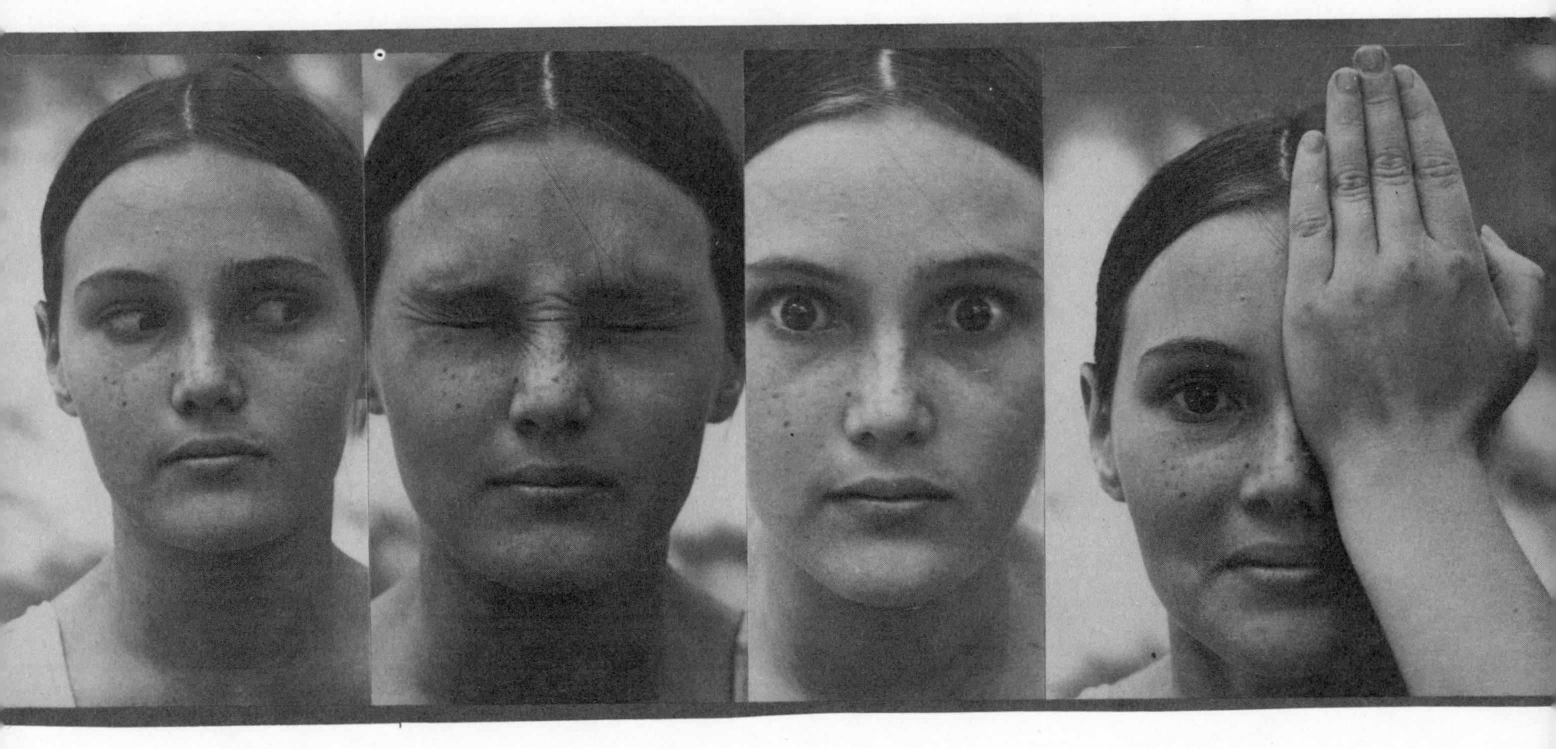

#21
Move the eyes as far to the side as possible and rotate the eyeballs

#22
Close the eyes very tight, then open as wide as possible, pushing the eyeballs outward as you EXHALE deeply.

#23
Place the heel of each hand directly on the closed lids and press hard, move the eyes against this resistance to strengthen and clear the eyes.

24 25 26

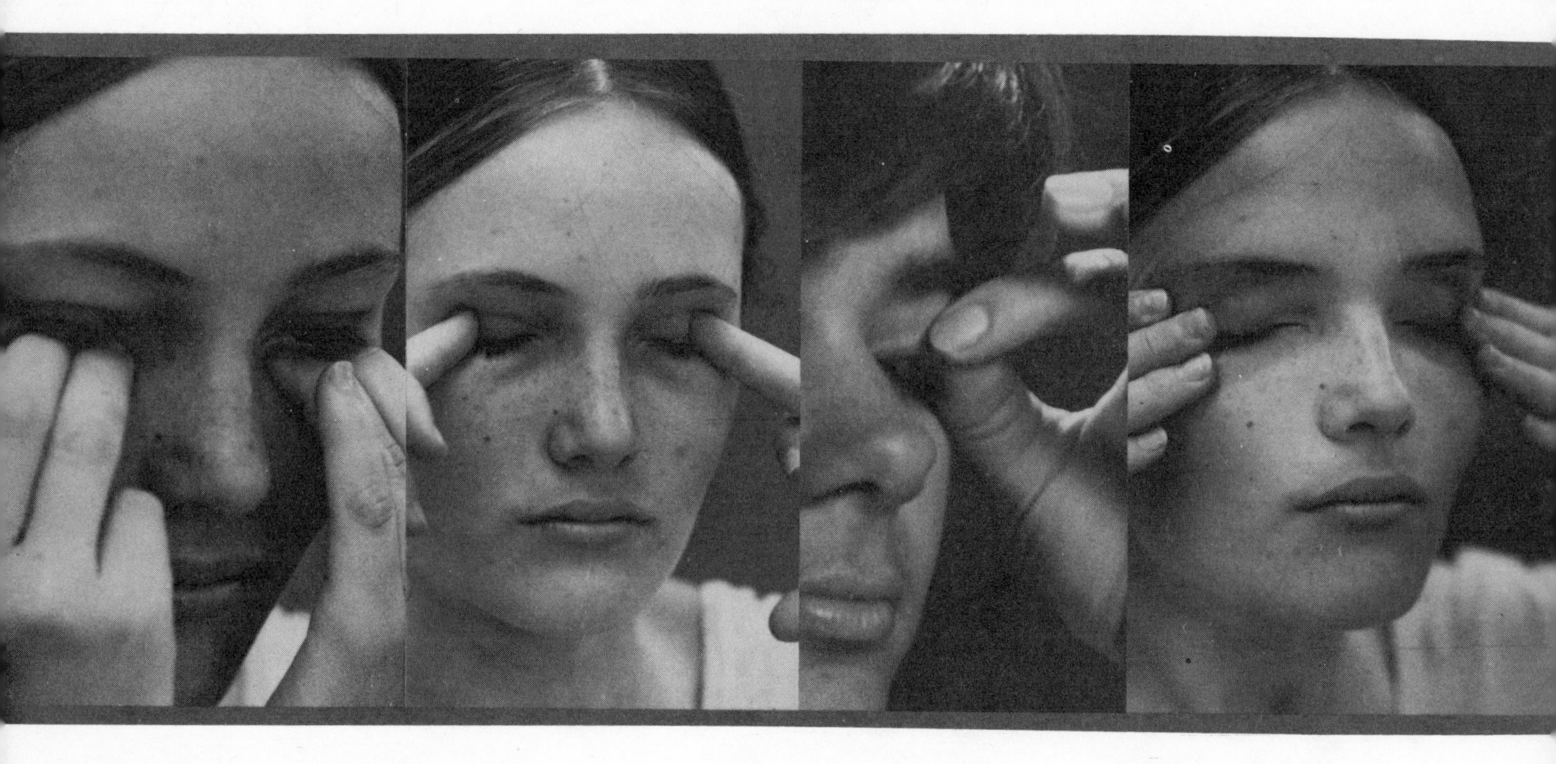

#24
With the eyelids closed, rhythmically push in the fingers (3rd and 4th) first above the eyeballs (Not shown) and then below (illustrated) Continue with the major finger only and press eyeballs closer toward the inside, if pain is felt, kidneys and bladder are low in Ki.

#25
Pinch and pluck the eyelid.
Making a vertical fold in the lid between thumb and index tip, pull lid away from the eye until a noise like a dripping fawcet is heard

#26
Drain the eyes of excess moisture

Using gentle to firm pressure of the finger-tips brush away the water brought there by the last 6 massages.

27 28 29

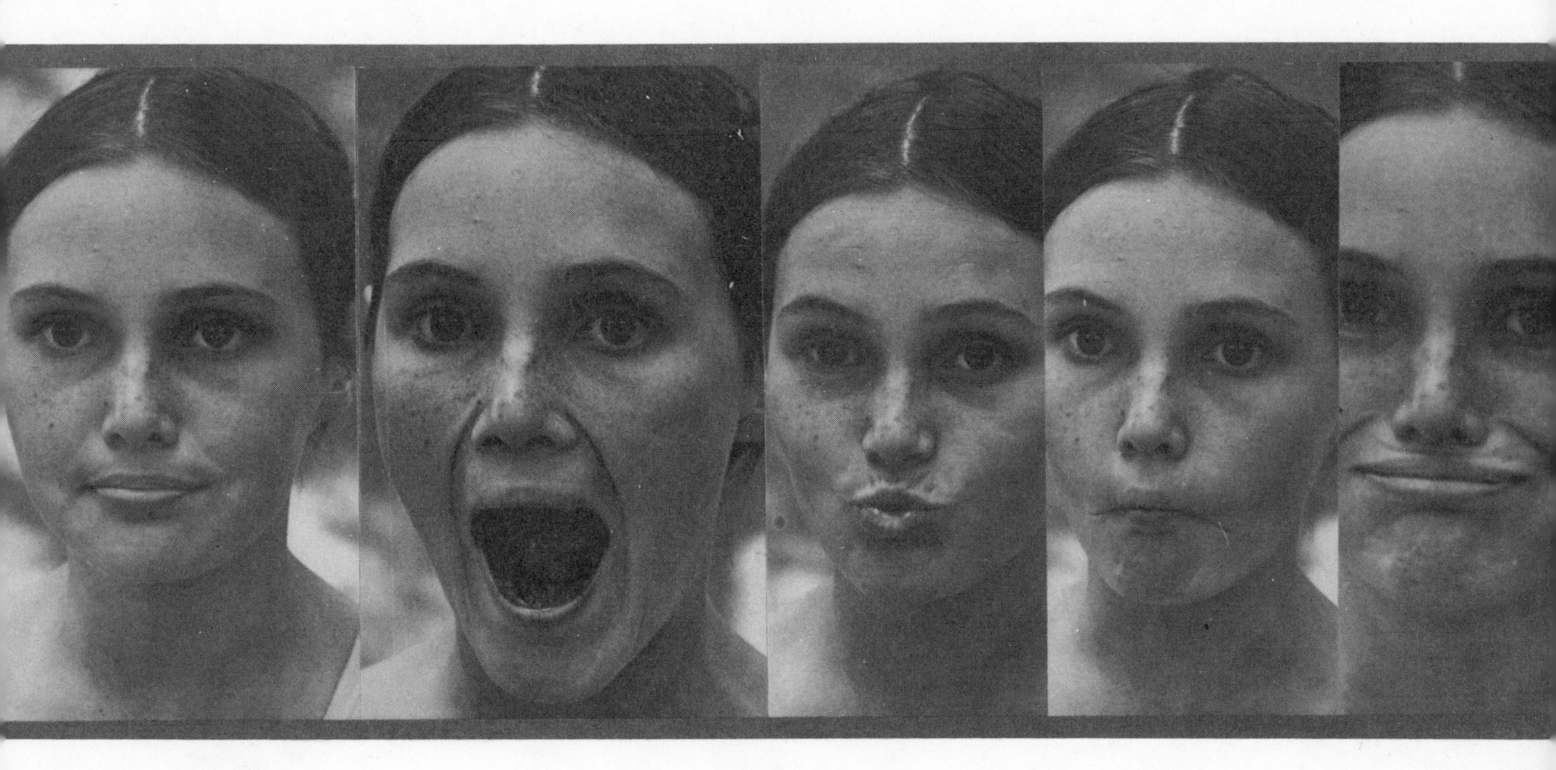

#27 INHALE
Pursing the lips then tighten the mouth muscles. Clamp the teeth together until pain is felt
EXHALE
and open the mouth as wide as possible

#28
Pout, then rotate the point of the lips all around...

...suck in the cheeks hard INHALE then through the pursed lips let the air EXHALE.

Make a loud Bronx cheer, vibrating the lips in a flutter.

30 **31** **32**

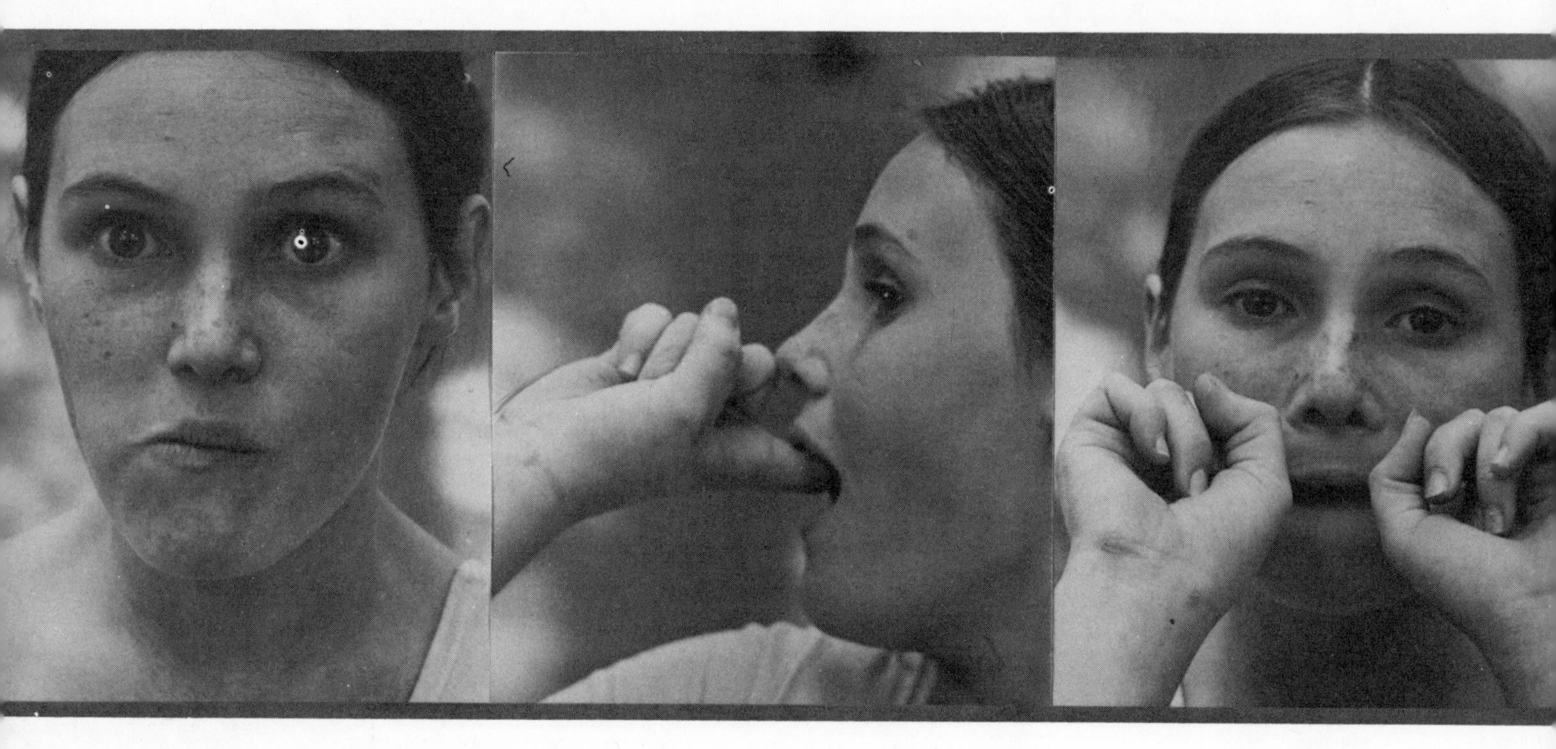

#30
With the tongue pressed hard against the outside of the gums and teeth, run it around the mouth and rub the cheeks from inside, hard.

#31 Hook into the palate...
With one finger crooked into the soft flesh area in the upper rear of the roof, pull and massage forward, gagging is expected the first few times

#32
Massage the inner corners of the mouth. With extended indexes, locate and rub the bony points found above the molars, then place the fingertip in the space at the rear of the last molar and bite hard with the wisdom teeth .
Stomach and Small Intestine meridians are stimulated.

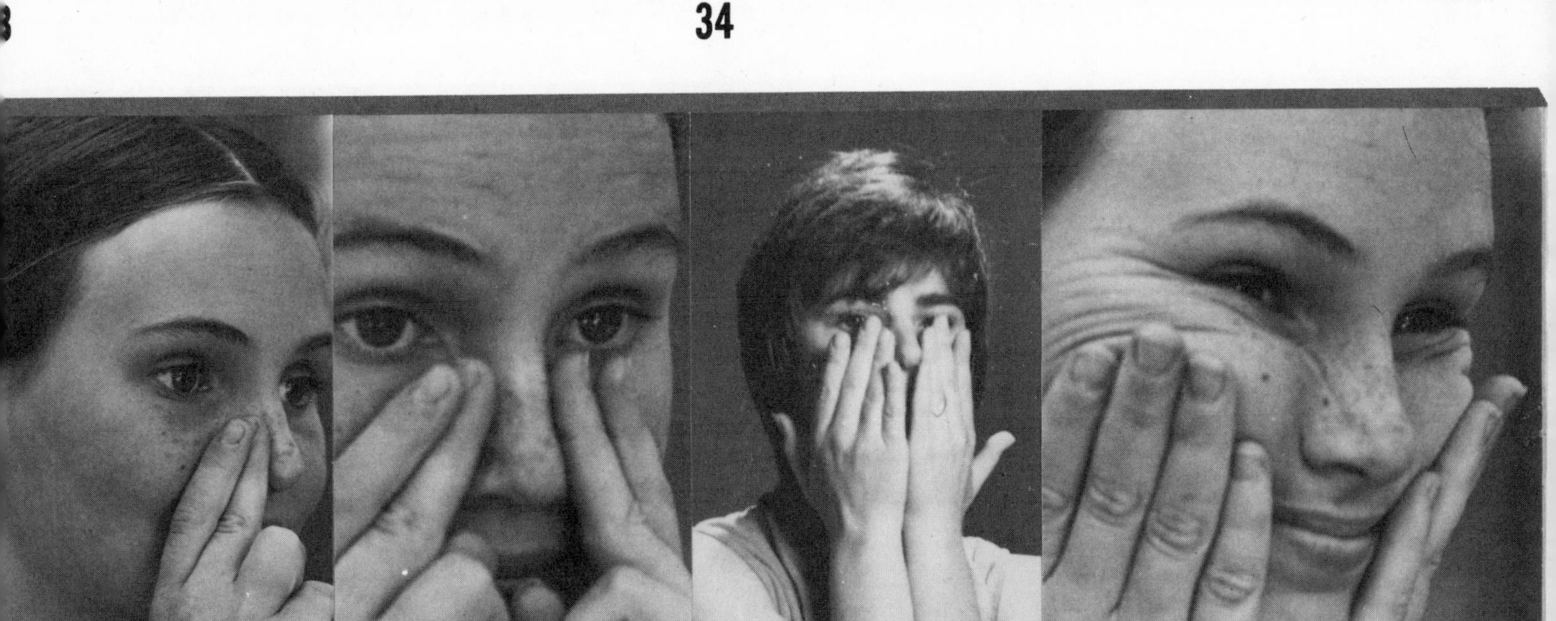

3 Rub the Nostrils
th the index on
p of the major
nger, rub upward
om the flare of the
se to its bridge... then squeeze the
cartilage below
the corner of the
eyes
INHALE & EXHALE
It is normal for
some excess moisture
and mucous to be
expelled, wipe off, then... #34

rub upward on
the cheekbones,
roll the flesh.

...finish by a strong
uppercut delivered with
the heel of the hand at
the jawbones.

35

36

37

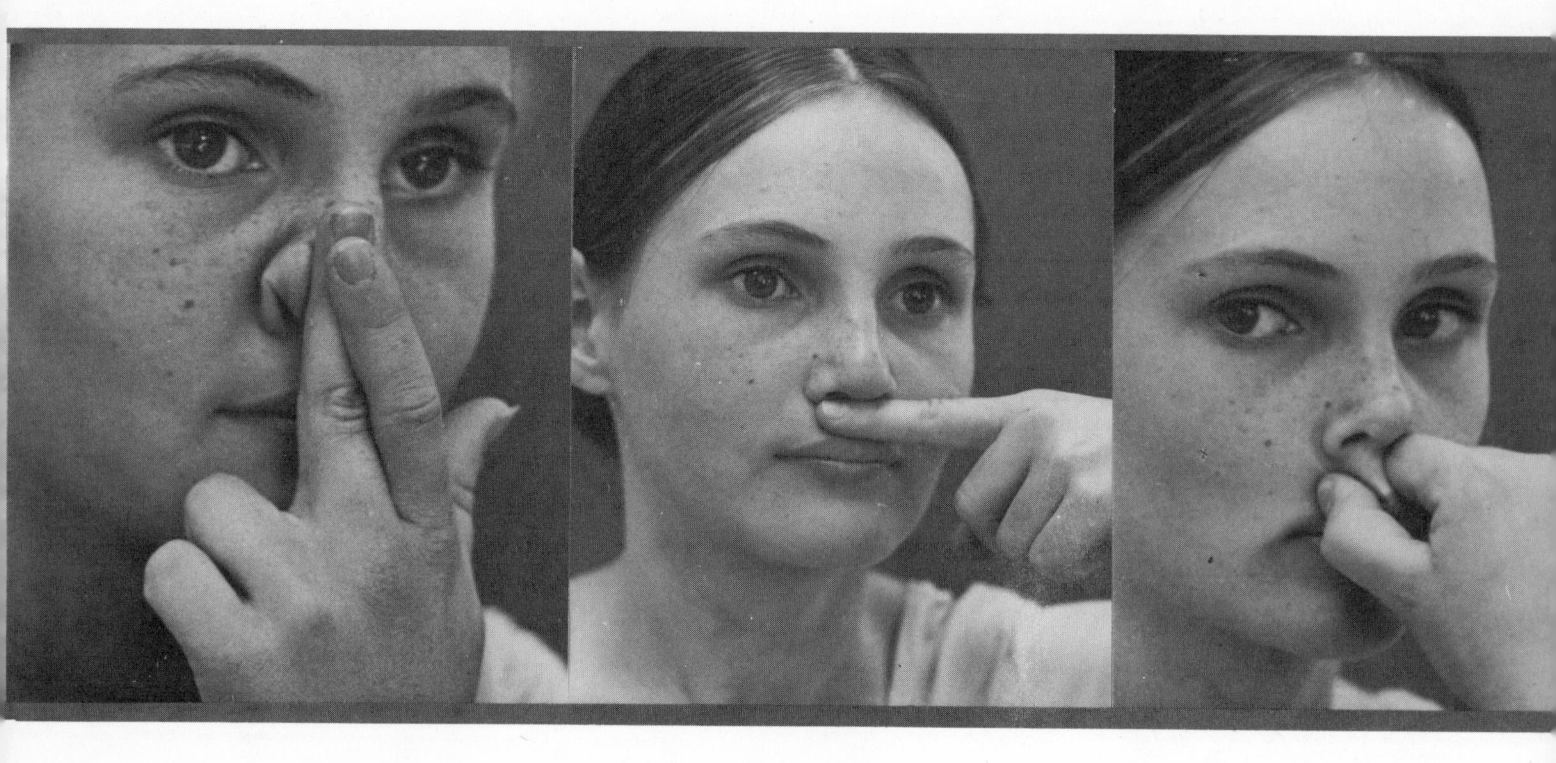

#35
Using the major finger, flatten the nose tip, then bend left and right, rotate and push upward. Restore the original flexibility to this important organ...

#36
Use the index or better the major finger to press hard under the nose, push and pull the finger rapidly until the cartilage cracks.

#37
Pinch the upper lip, (the parallel vertical fc relates to the sex organs and pull hard first right then left and shake the excess moisture off.

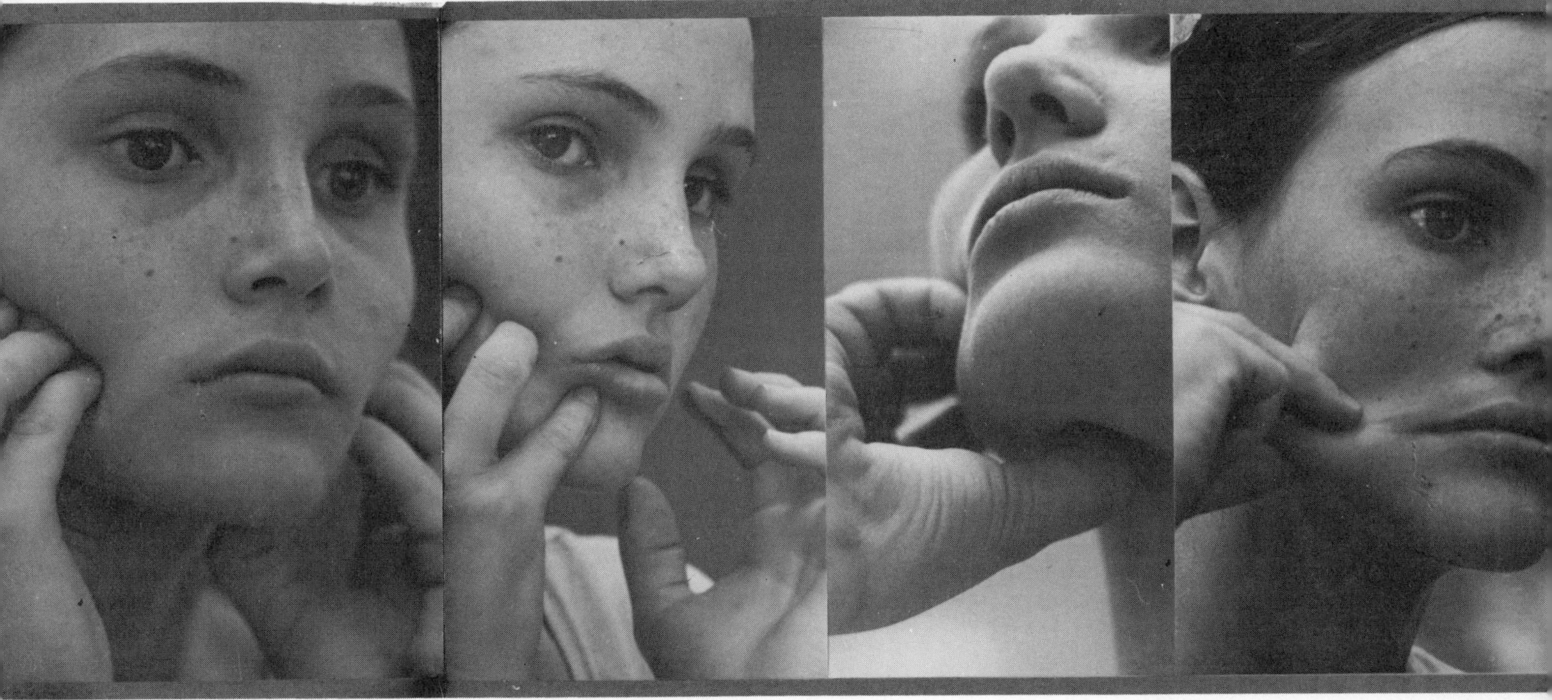

#38
Percussion on the gums.

Pressing all fingers, (or the fingernails) into the cheeks, feel for the root of the teeth, place the thumbs under the jawline and reduce the double chin production.
... drumming with the fingertips on the same areas further stimulates the Small and Large intestine as well as the stomach meridians.

...the thumb now reaches to the center of the chin underside, Massage deeply or place index and major inside the mouth bottom and squeeze (Affects Heart meridian.)

#40 Milk the Corner of the Jaw

Grasp and pull the fleshy cheek near the jaw hinge, EXHALE as you pull and milk the excesses.

41 42 43

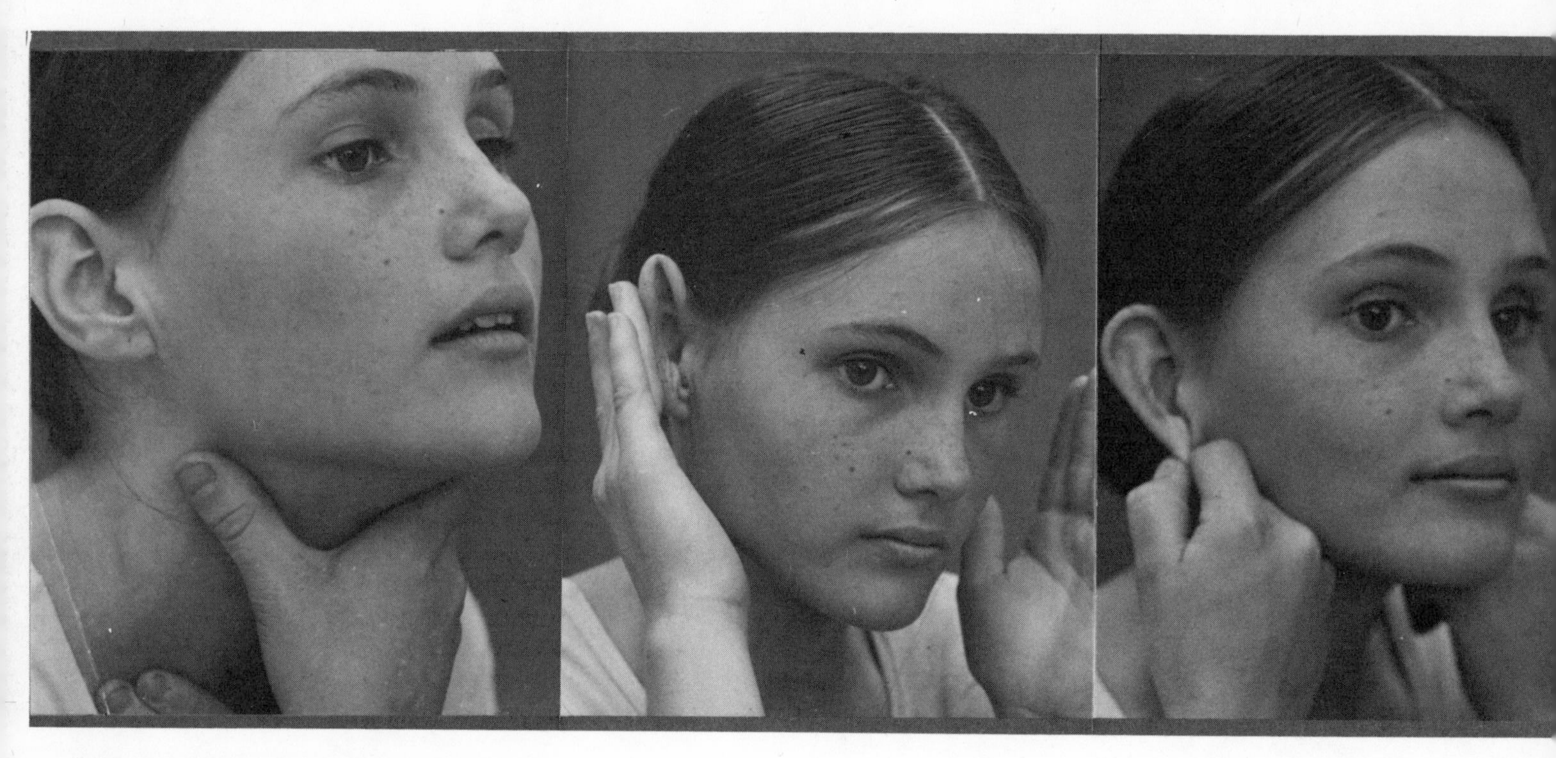

$41
Beautiful "Old Ladies" remain Wrinkle-free... when the neck down to the thyroid is massaged daily. Begin just under the jawbone and finish by inserting two fingers around the gland at the center of the collarbone Spontaneous coughing is a normal reaction.

#42
Flip the ears forward

Beginning with the little finger, bend the ears forward and flatten them hard against the side of the head, brush forward repeatedly.

#43
Pull the earlobes down

Tugging at the ears is often a sign of indecisic regain a sure sense of direction and hearing...

44 45

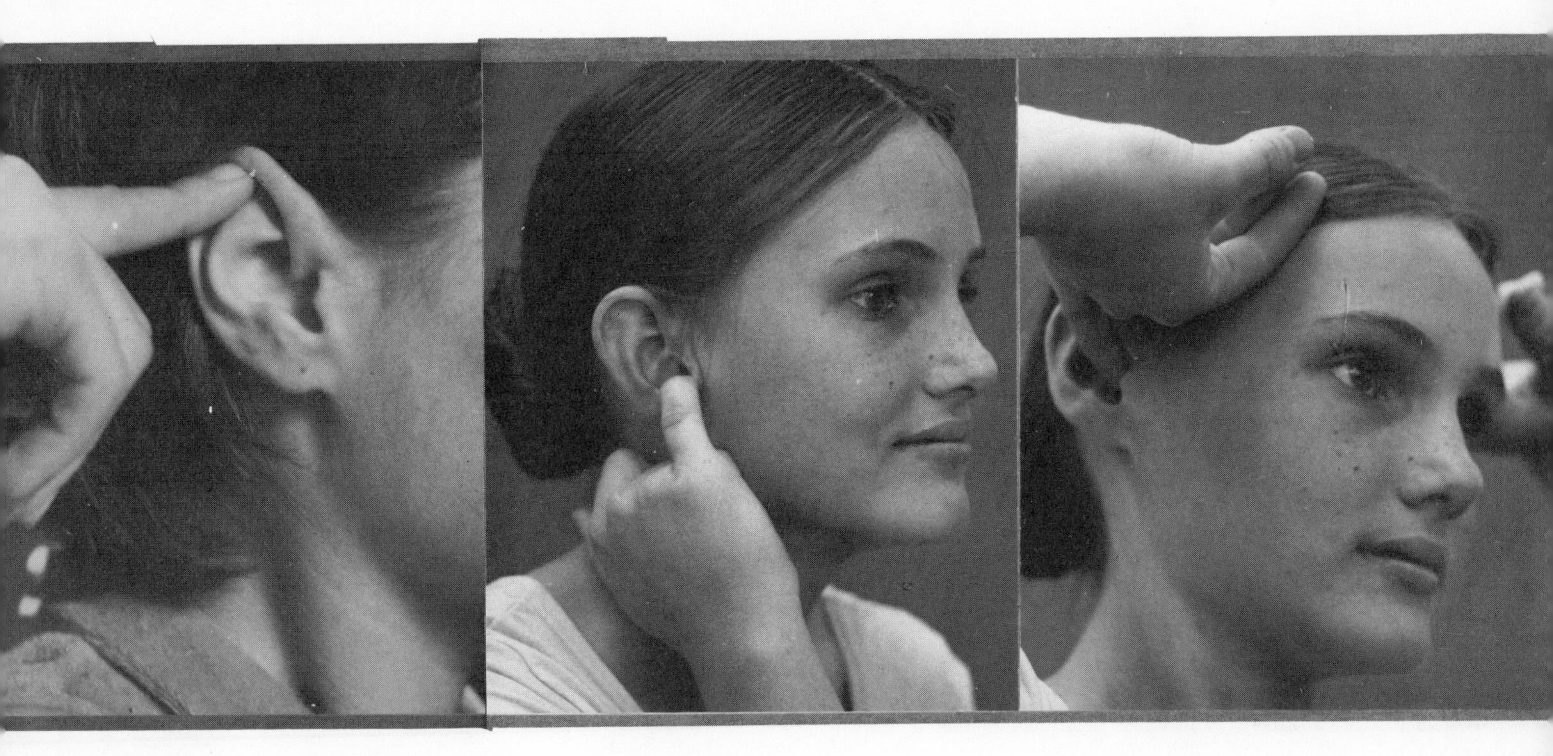

#44 Tracing the Spiral of the Ear

Using the tip of the major finger, rub all around the spiral channel of the ear. .

then hook the little finger into the eardrum hole and pull in all four direction in succession: Up, down, frontward and backward. Finish by pulling and rotating the small bony flap (the Tragus) which is in front of the ear opening.

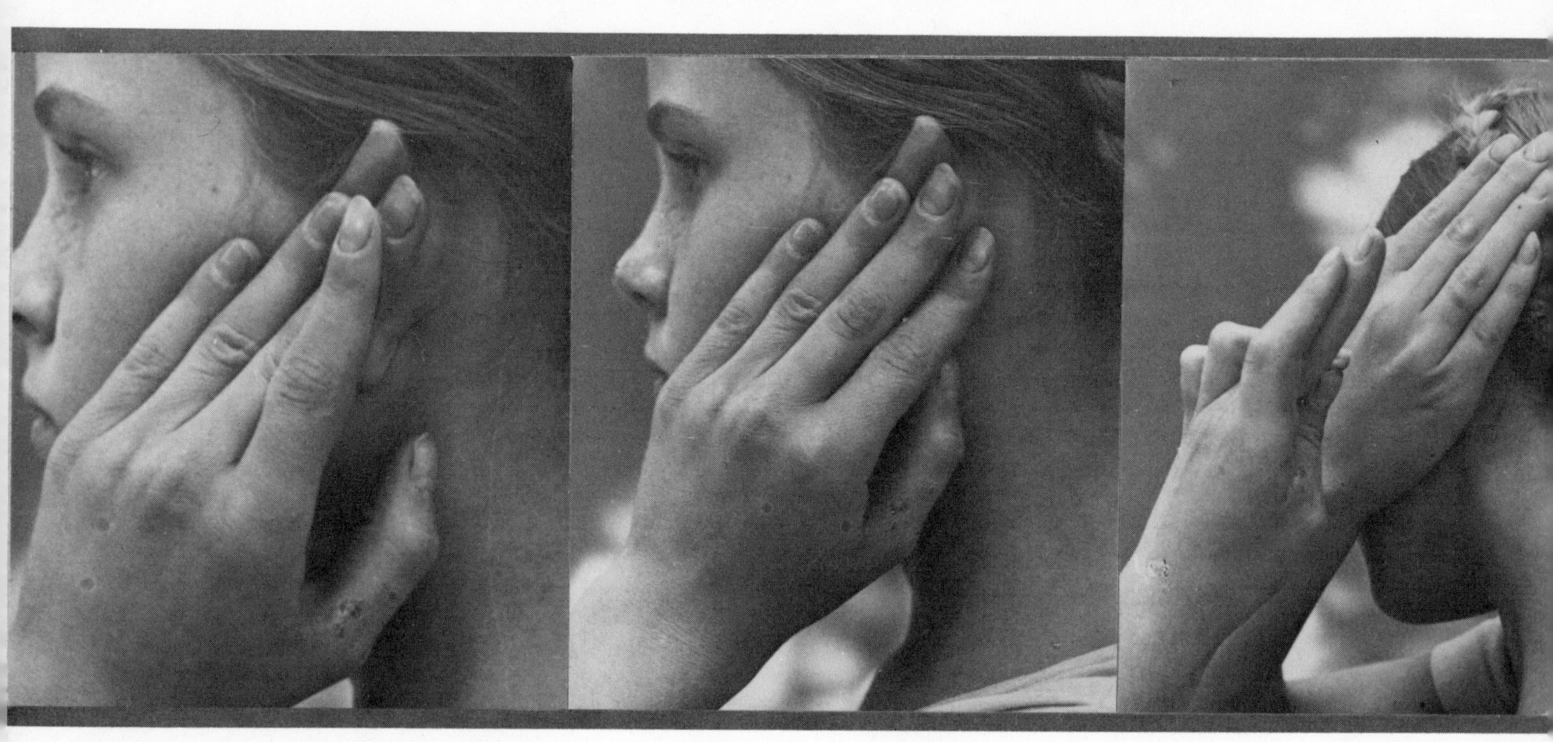

#46
Heavenly Drum Sound...
is heard when the ears are flattened against the head by the 3rd, 4th and 5th finger and flicking the index off the major in order to strike the mastoid area...

...the sound heard at this point give an accurate account of the condition of the Gall Bladder and of the Triple Warmer organs.

#47
The Conch Shell sound
Cupping one hand over the ear and hitting the hollow shell with two fingers of the other han
Treats the kidneys and energizes the Triple War

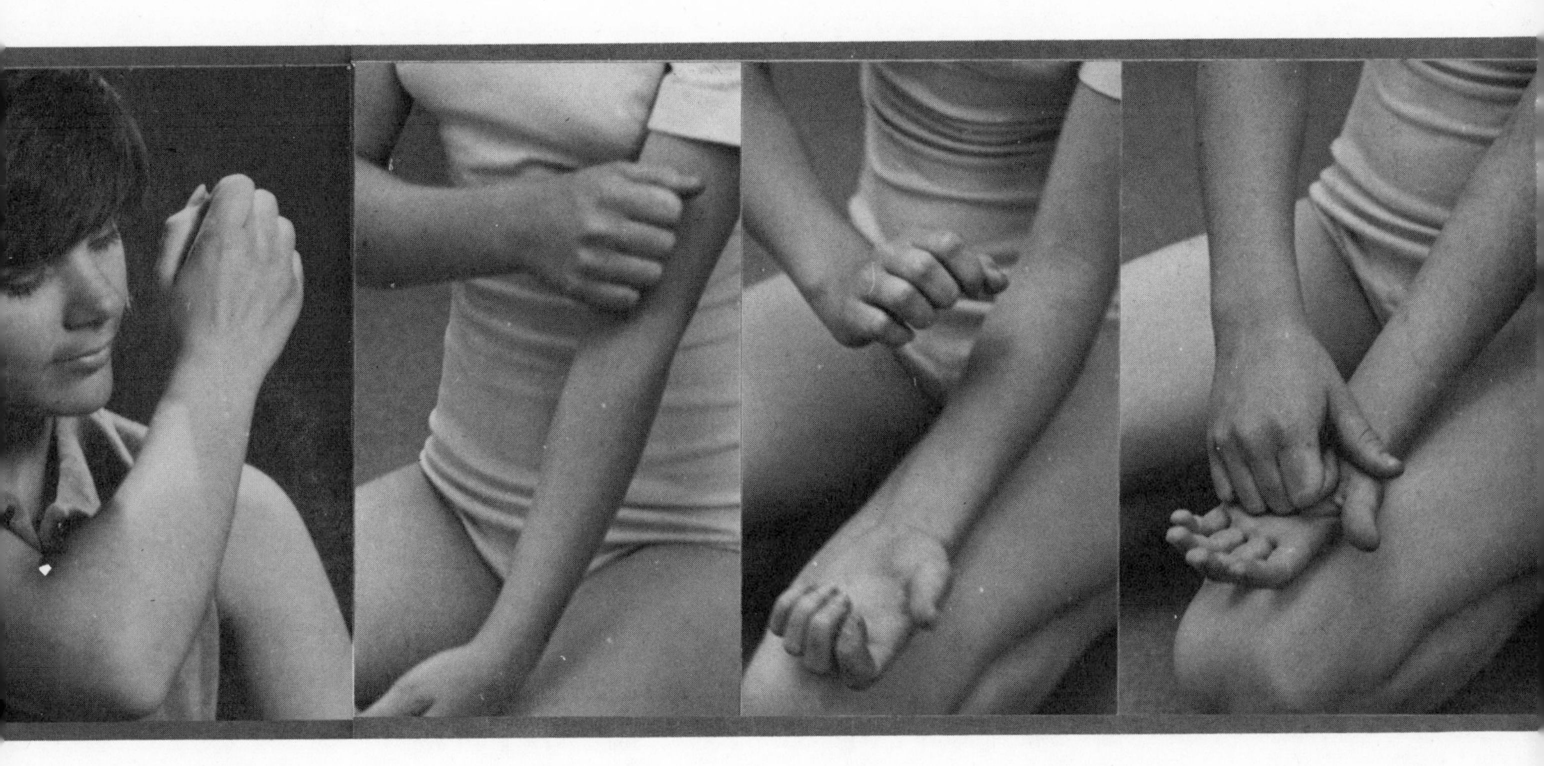

48
ercussion on the
pper members

eginning at the side of
he neck, the hand should
trike lightly, using only
he weight of the loose
ist hinged at the wrist
.s a small flexible hammer...continue on down the arm
and linger at the elbow fold,
varying the force of the strike
depending on the reaction (pain)
...the forearm as well
as the wrist possess
many acupoints in need
of stimulation:
(see left side chart
page 93.)

The relaxed opened
palm receives some
additional drumming
(Lungs and Heart)

Always applaud with
gusto!

49 50 51

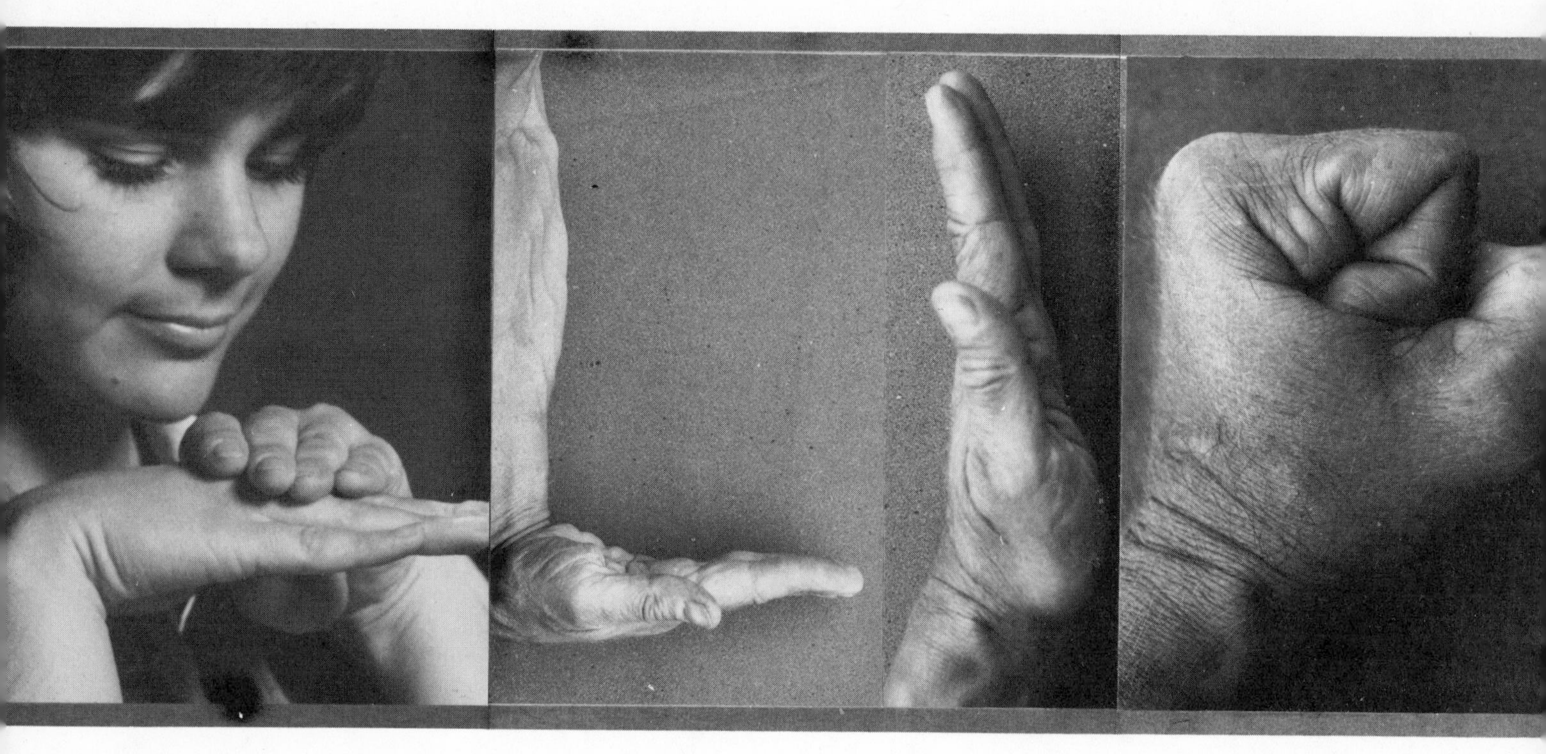

#49
The Wrist Fold

An ability to bend the wrist at a perfect right angle is a sign of good condition of an organism, test yourself and maintain this vital trait

#50
.. a backward bend is just as important and should reach the same sharp right angle...

#51
Holding the hand straight up with a little tension should bend the fingers naturally back a little...

Pulling the hand into a fist should make a perfect square, movements of open and closed fist (3rd & 4th photos) are helpful to restore.

52 53

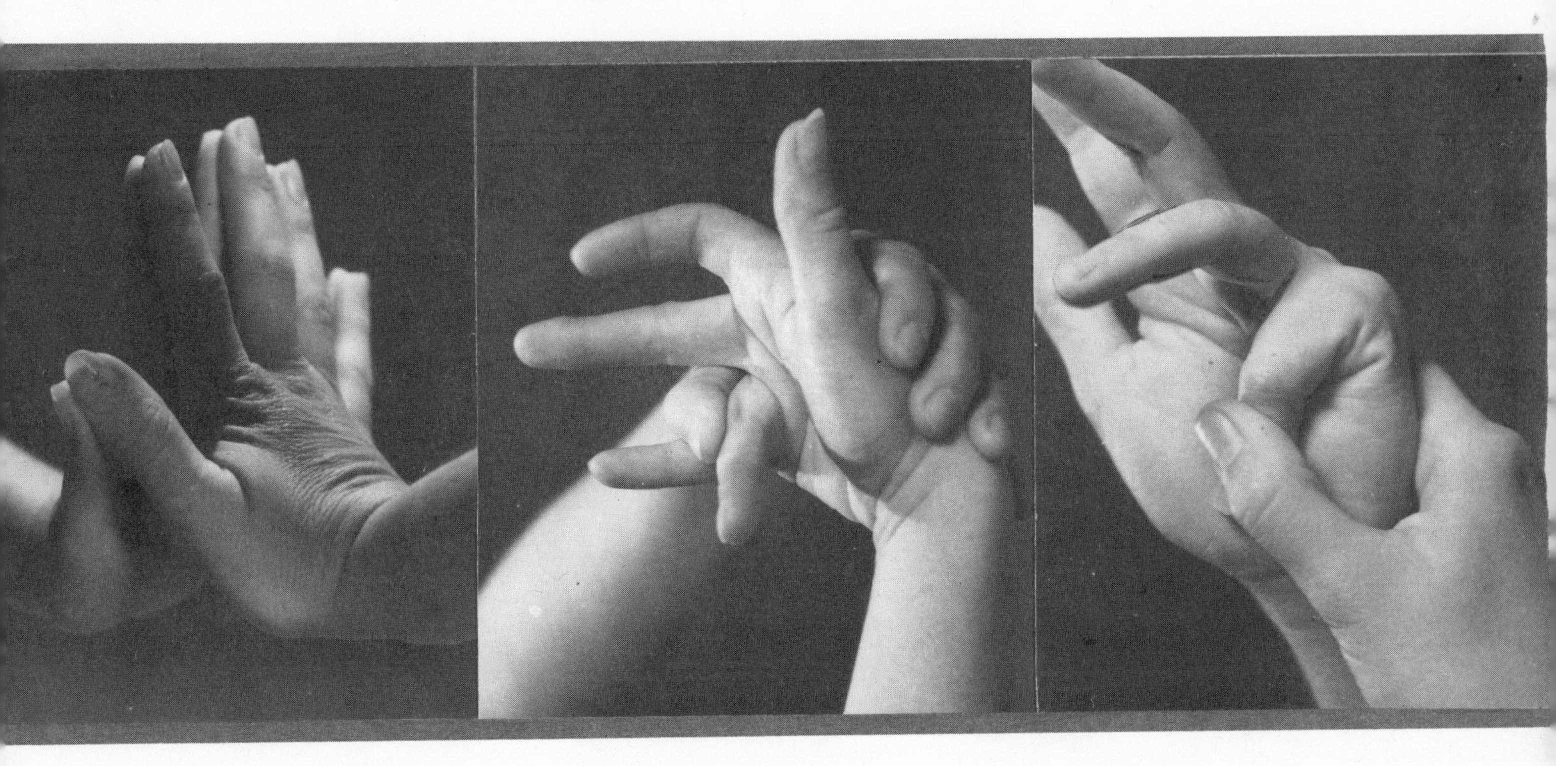

#52
Bend the fingers and the wrists backward

Flexibility through the exercising of the finger joints is very vital to the discharge of toxins.

Place the hands as shown and raise elbows high and hard.

#53

Bend fingers to the palm and crack them. Lay one hand in the other and force each° finger with the thumb until a snap sound in heard.
Promotes the free flow of ki energy.

See "Fingers and Toes, the polarity changes" page 43.

54 55 56

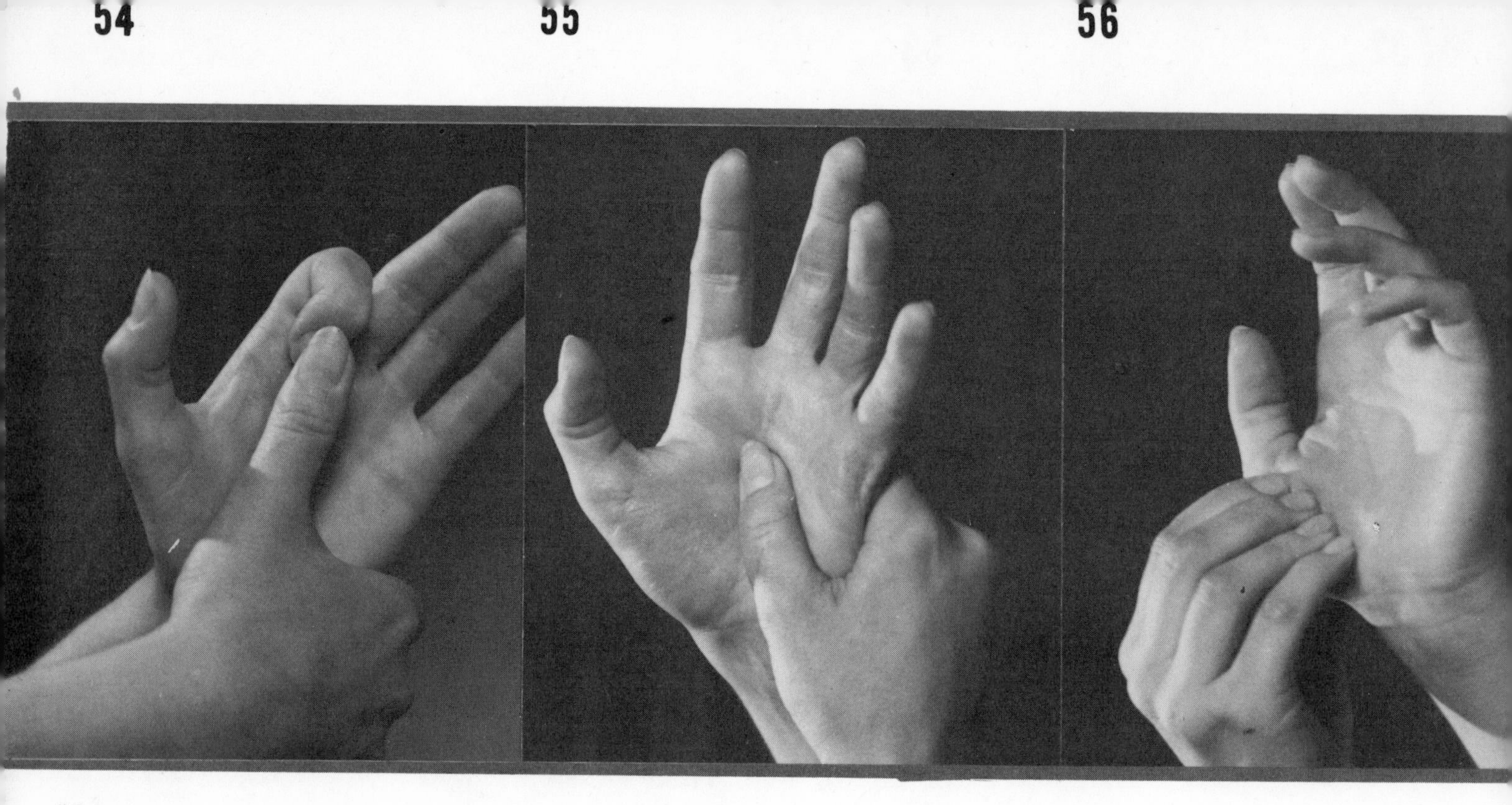

#54

Cracking the nail joint

Grasp the wrist with the four fingers of one hand and use the thumb to bend the last joint at the point of each finger.

#55

Deep thumb pressure all over the palm of each hand. Cup or wrap the palm around the massaging finger in order to increase the penetration.

#56

The fleshy shank of the thumb contains the meridian of the lungs (Lp 9 and Lp 10) Deep massage or percussion of this area for colds, flu, or any lung ailments.

(See page 46 to 49)

#57
Hook and pull fingers

Link each pair of fingers and pull apart, move arms left and right under pressure.

#58
Push away and flick the wrists

Maintain or restore the flexibility of the wrists and discharge the accumulated toxins blocking the articulations.

59 **60**

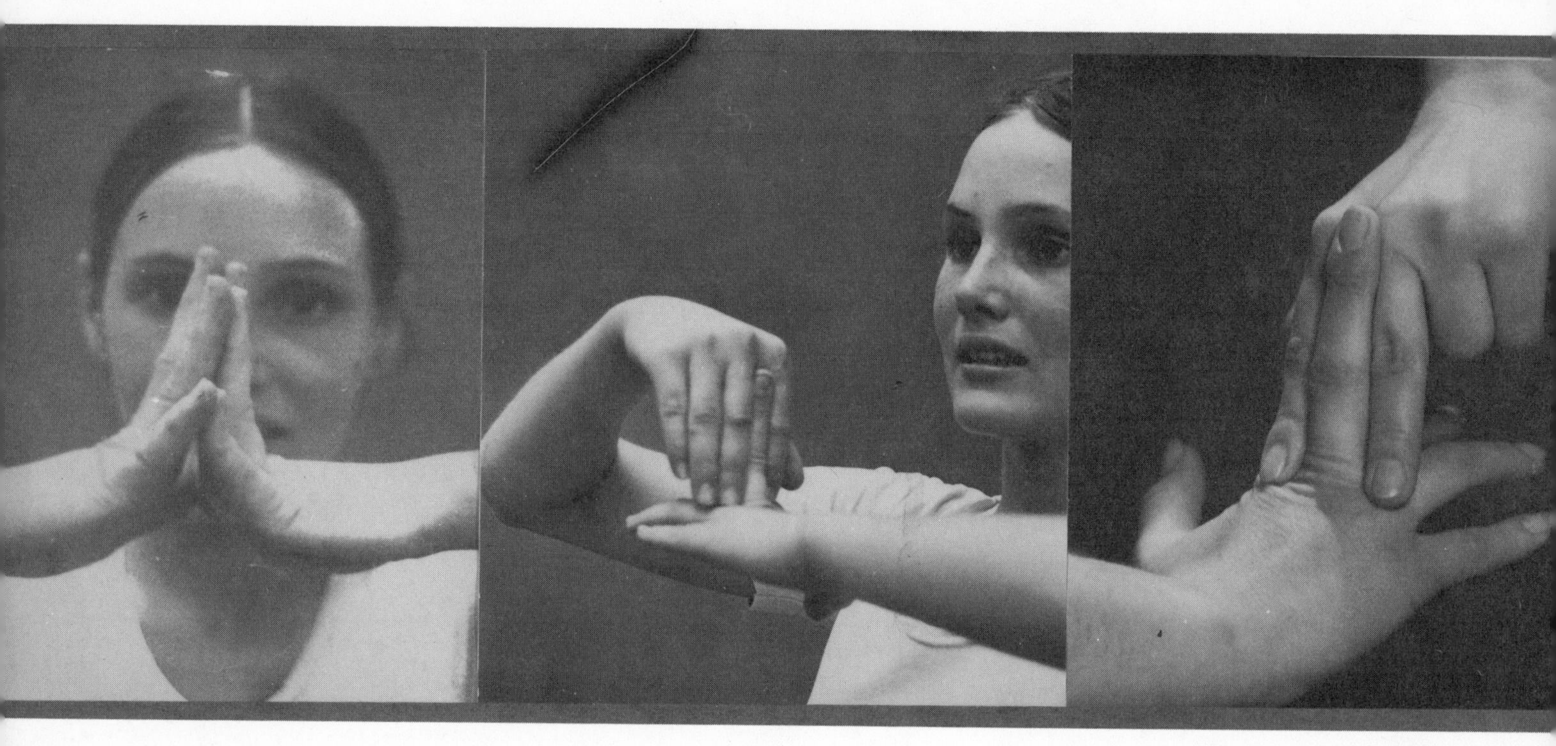

#59
Right angle bending

Between the flat of the hand and the fingers, the angle should reach 90°, warm up by pushing the fingers together, work on each group of two fingers back and forth at a time then...

#60

make a fork with the index and the major of the other hand and make each finger stand straight, a right angle means good condition of the joints

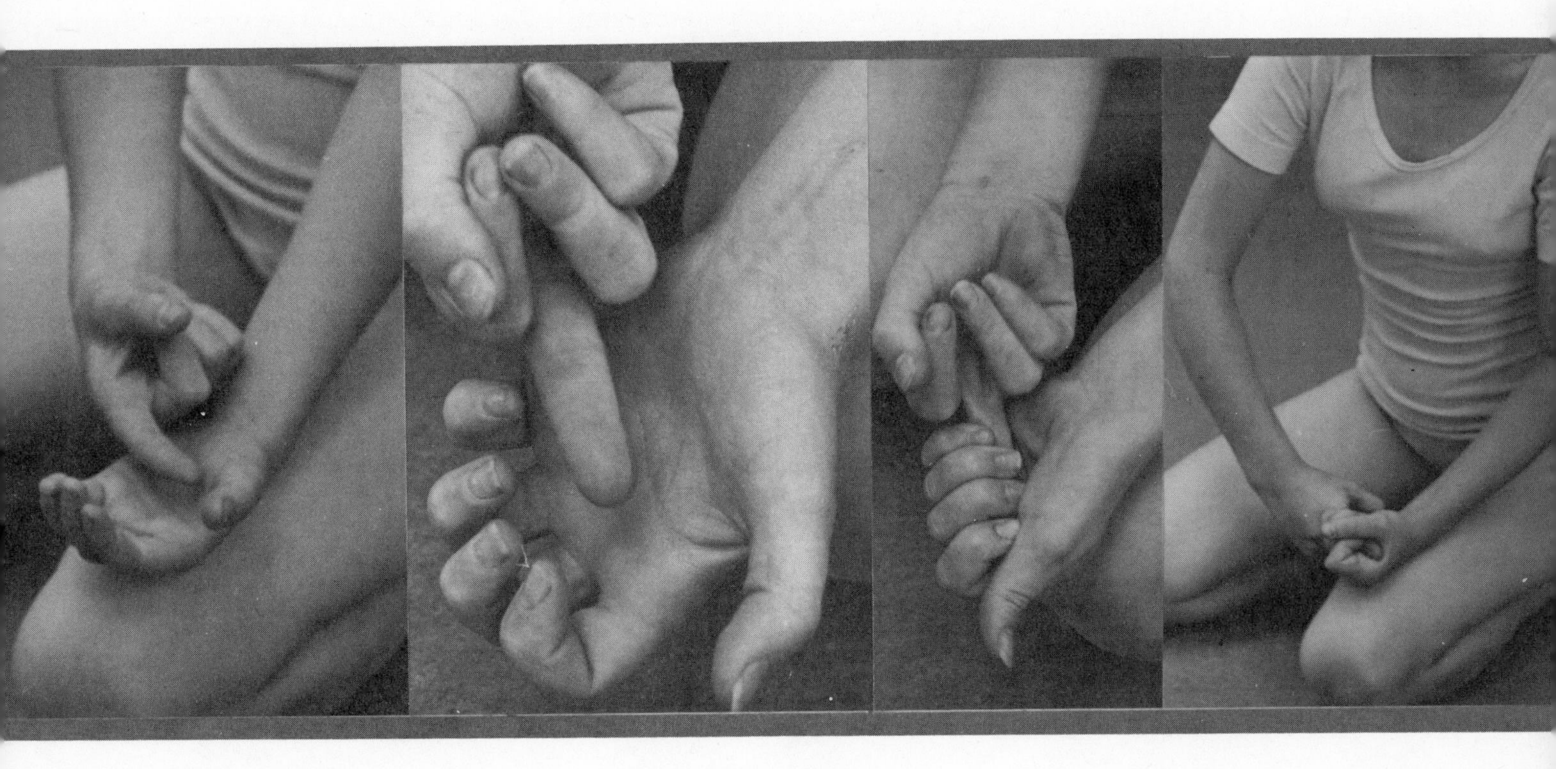

The Finger Vise

Each finger in turn is laid into the open vise of the opposite palm, wrapping all four fingers around, pull and twist the finger out, facing the palm of the pulling hand downward, repeat with the other hand.

(Note: The thumb is pulled also but the twisting goes in the other direction.)

62 63 64

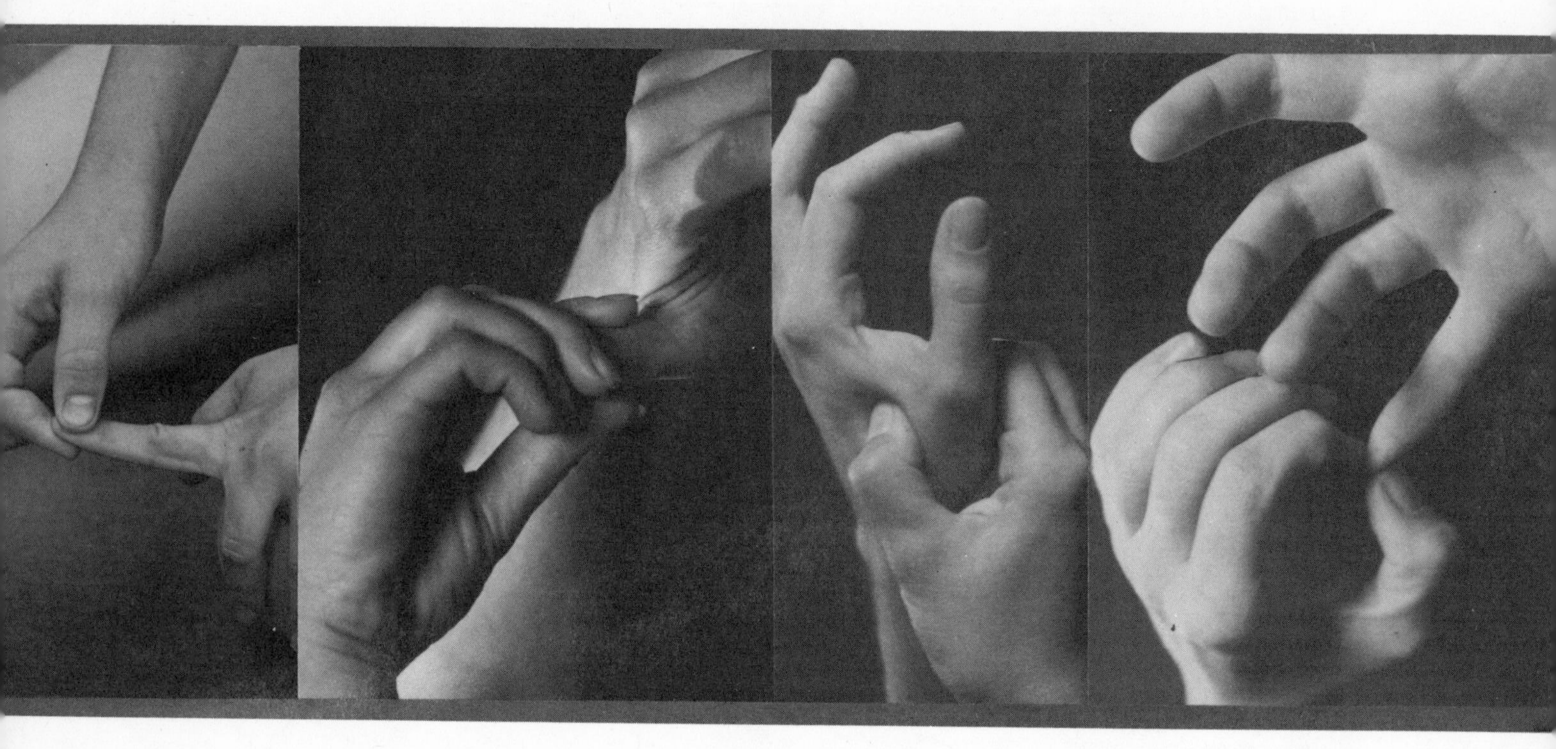

#62
Rotate the
fingers

First pull out
then rotate
each finger at
the point where
it attaches to
the hand...

Also rotate the thumb
in both directions in
order to warm it up
for the next massage...

#63
Thoroughly knead
the "web" between
thumb and index

#64 Pinch each finger
at the nail corners

Repeat Exercises 5
and 58 before the next
breathing exercise (#65)

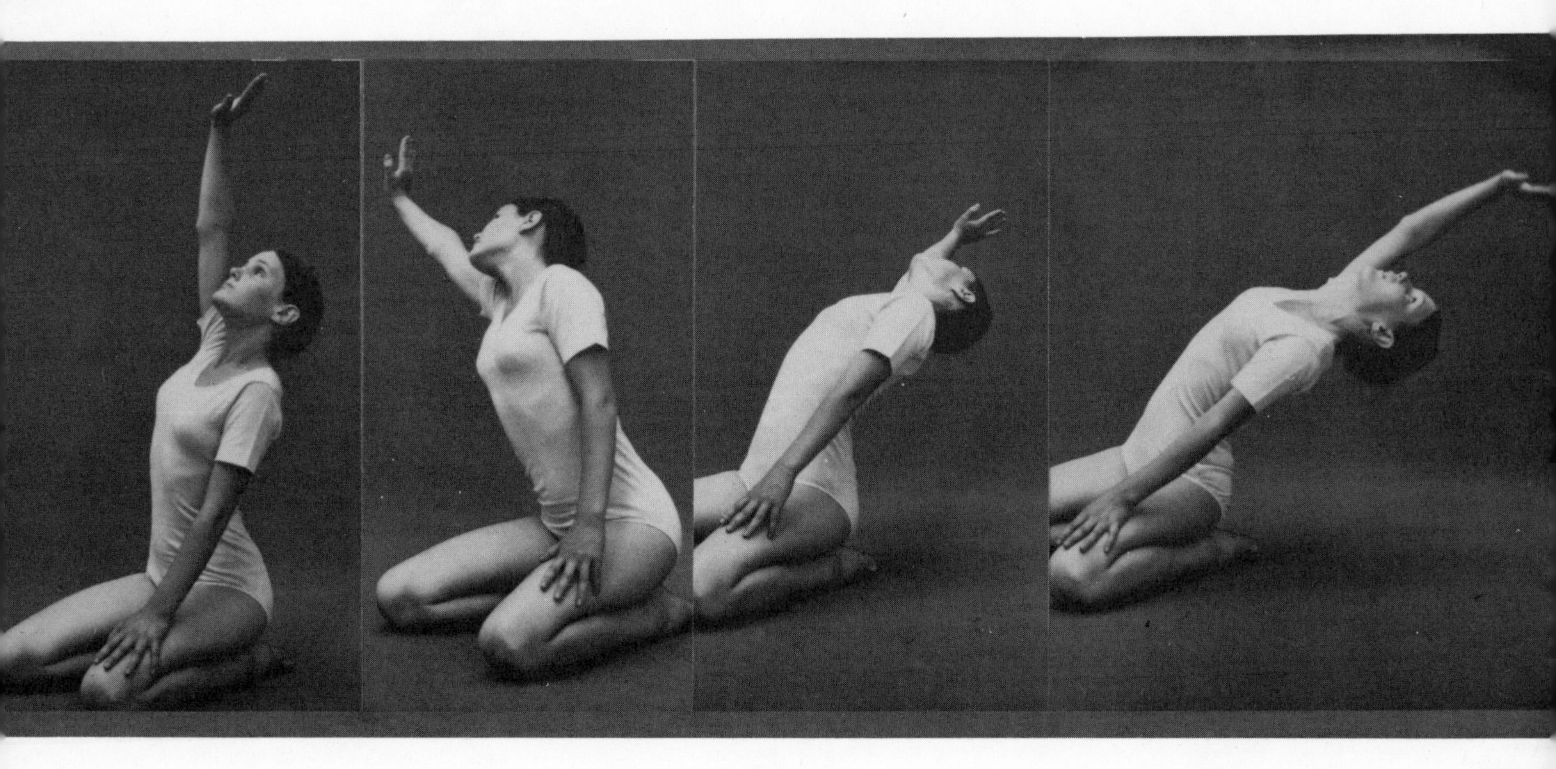

#65

REACH FOR THE BACK WALL

Sitting in seiza (buttocks on heels) and with the backbone very tall and straight. INHALE while lifting the hand overhead, palm facing up. Look up at the back of the hand and keep the eyes on that point throughout the rest of the exercise. Lean the trunk to the right, keeping the left buttock in contact with the left heel.

...lean backward as far as possible rotating the trunk clockwise up to center rear. Lean forward and EXHALE through the open mouth.

Note: Lift up the left hand and lean the trunk to the left, repeat the above but on the other side, counter clockwise rotation. 3x each side.

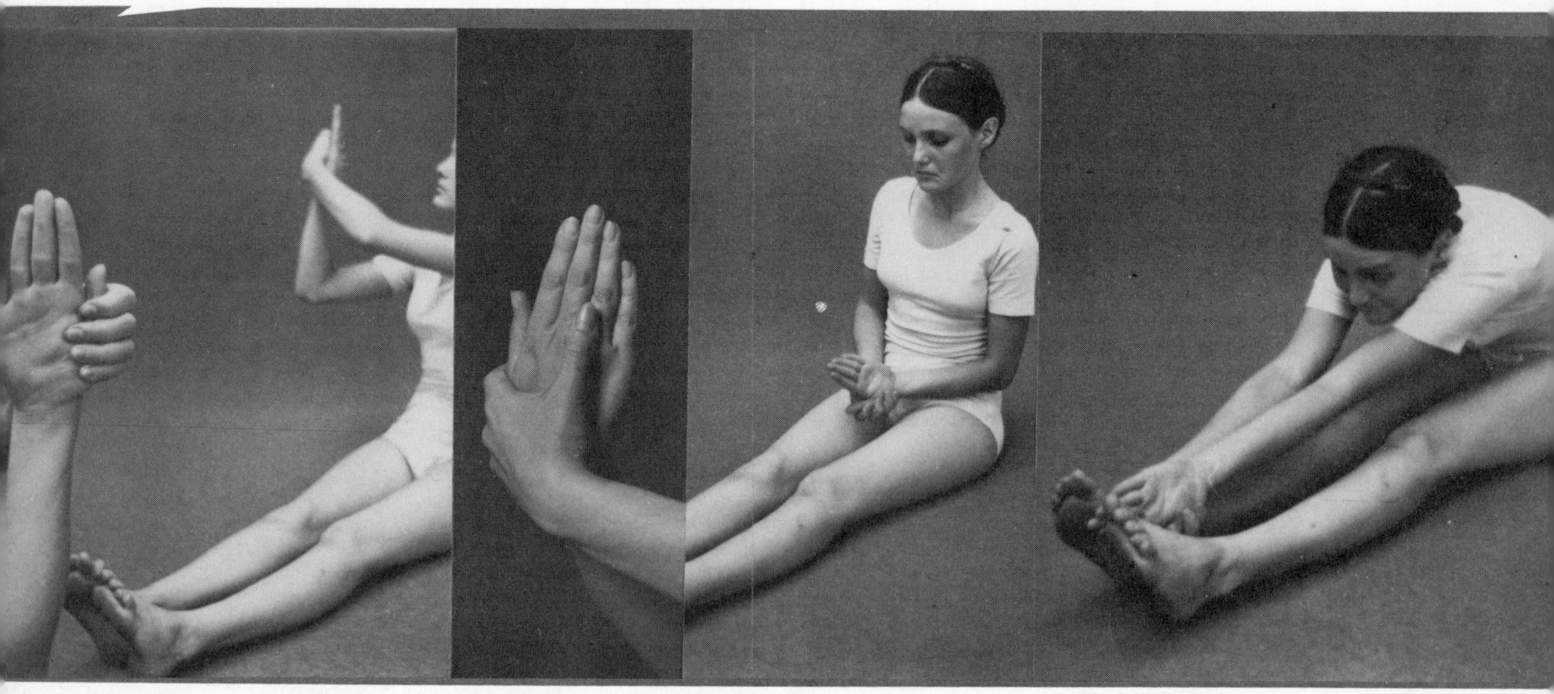

#66
Wrist twist Expeller

Float up the hand as shown by student at the right of first picture. Left hand grasps the thumb and forces the hand to turn outward...

INHALE
Bring both hands close to the navel still twisting
Bend both hands forward, pointing the fingers toward the toes forcefully... begin

EXHALING and stretch forward still keeping the twisting grasp on

Note: Repeat with the other hand

3x each side

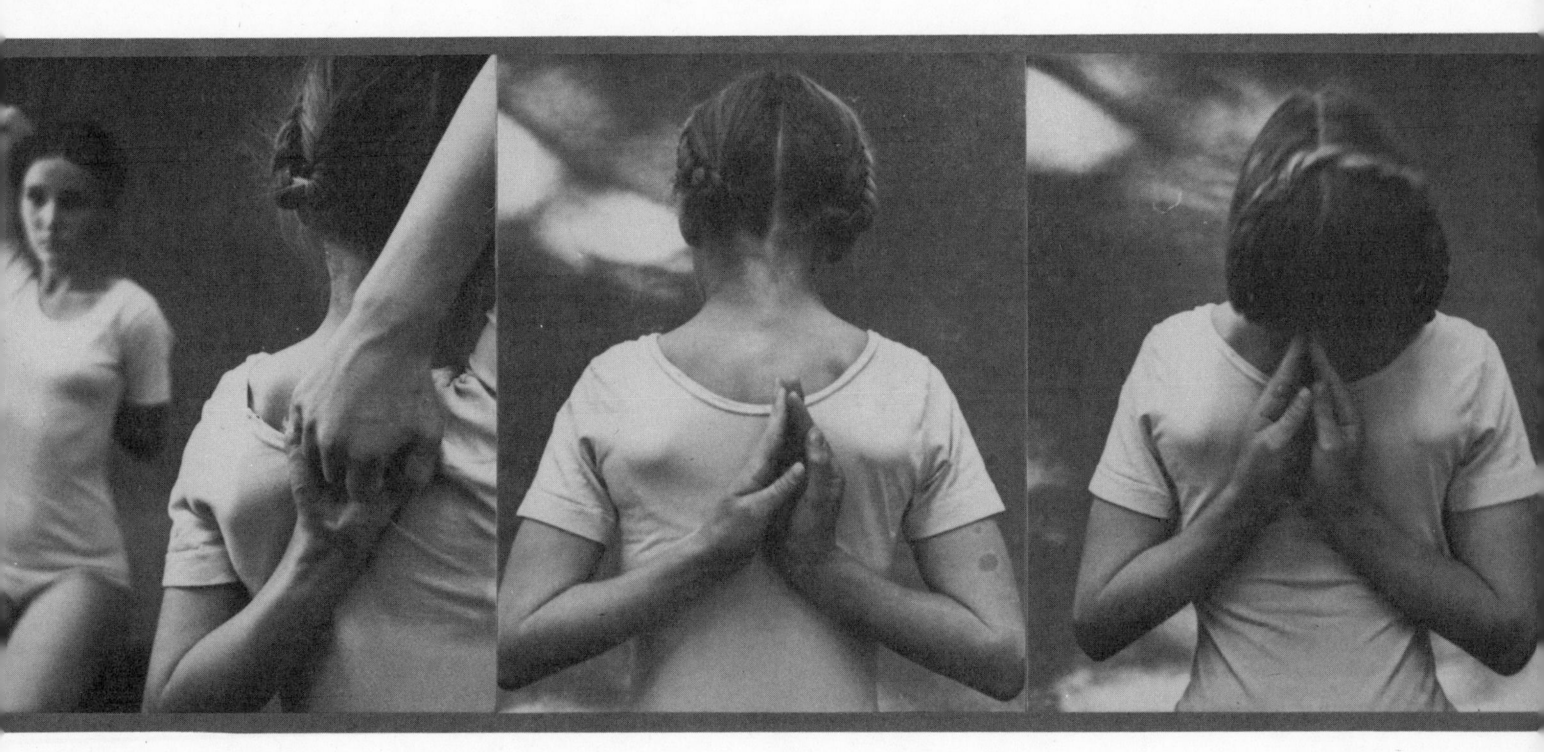

#67

SHOULDER BLADE WARM-UP

Right arm overhead and forearm behind the head. Lift up left arm (Back of hand touching the left shoulder blade, touch the fingertip or as shown at right of first photo) Link the fingers or clasp the wrists with the fingers.

#68
Join the palms in the back

Place both hands together in the back at waist level, raise both hands as high as possible at the height of the shoulder blades, bend the wrists alternatively...
then continue raising the hands until they touch the back of the head, tilted back or standing tall...!

69 70 71

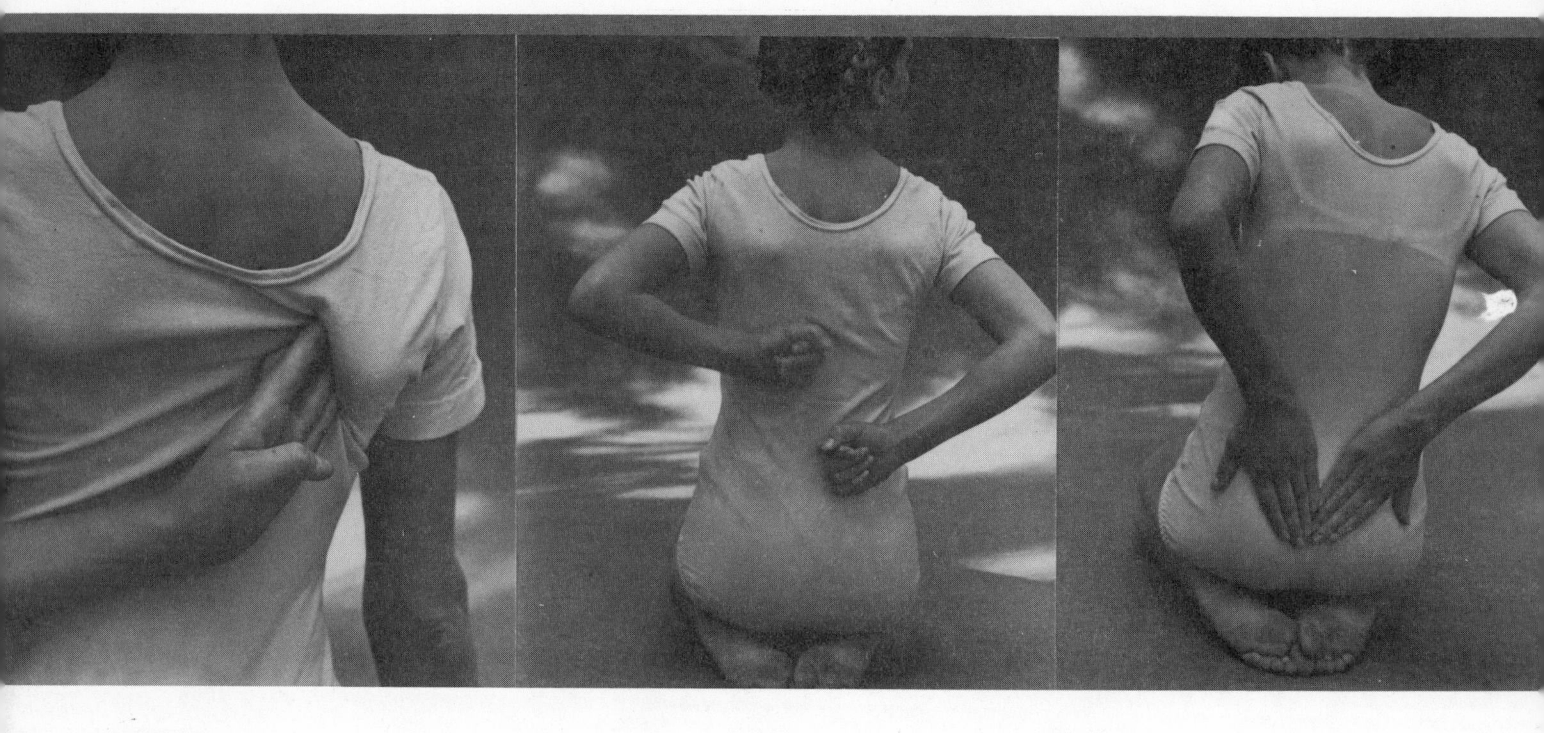

#69
Place the left hand at the edge of the right shoulderblade as shown. Relax the right arm and insert the stiff fingertips under the cleavage, move the fingers all around and under, clearing and cleaning all deposits and coagulated proteins. Repeat with the other side.

Note: In order to first break through, it helps sometimes to have someone else do the first insertion.

#70
Drumming on the back

INHALE then beat with the closed fists on the back up and down. EXHALE forcefully while twisting the head sideways and open the mouth wide

#71
Rub the base of the spine

With both hands flat on the back and sustained pressure, massage up and down until warm and the skin reddens.

72 73 74a

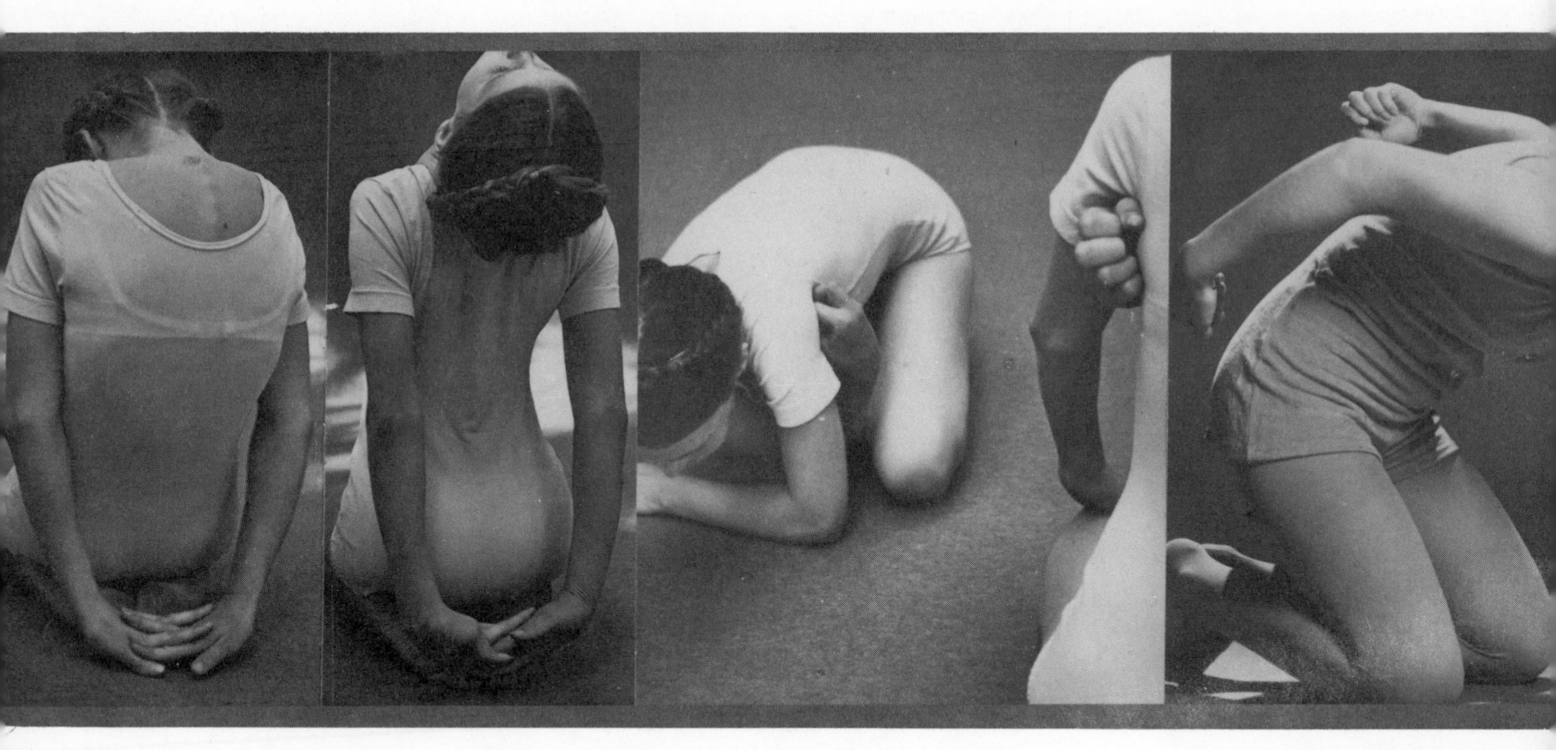

#72

EXPAND AND CONTRACT THE BACKSIDE

INHALE, and link fingers together in the back. Under the toes if possible otherwise lay the palms on the sole of the feet. EXHALE while pushing the shoulders forward and the head down making a "round" back. INHALE (Second photo) With hands still clasped, bring the shoulderblades together and throw the head back EXHALE and return to the upright, relaxed position.

#73

Small Intestine Acupoint

In the seiza posture, lean over and place one elbow on the floor, the knuckles of the other hand first locate the sensitive Sig 9 point, then, using percussion, treat until pain lessens or dissapears
(see page 65 to 67.)

#74a

THE SPANKING

Spleen, stomach and Bladder acupoints located in and near the buttocks get very little stimulation... in the normal adult!

Gentle percussion using loose, hinged wrists.

#74b

The Third Expeller

Starting from the seiza posture, curl the toes under and lean the trunk forward until the chest touches the thighs, hands flat and stretched out on the ground in front while EXHALING.

The student in the background demonstrates the open jack knife forward projection during the EXHALING with open mouth.

Note: Hands remain in place throughout, body should not sag and touch the ground.

An alternate ending position is shown above:

The head twists sideways in order to mix-in the breath and force for air out of the lungs.

‡75

ℜaking the sides of the neck

Throw one hand across the chest and over the shoulder
as far as it will reach, hook the fingers and rake
the sides of the neck, keeping a constant pressure.
On the downstroke, the other hand is thrown in a
similar way with the breath expelled in short rhythmic
bursts.

Note: If the arms are very stiff and cannot reach far back, use one hand to push the hand lower down.

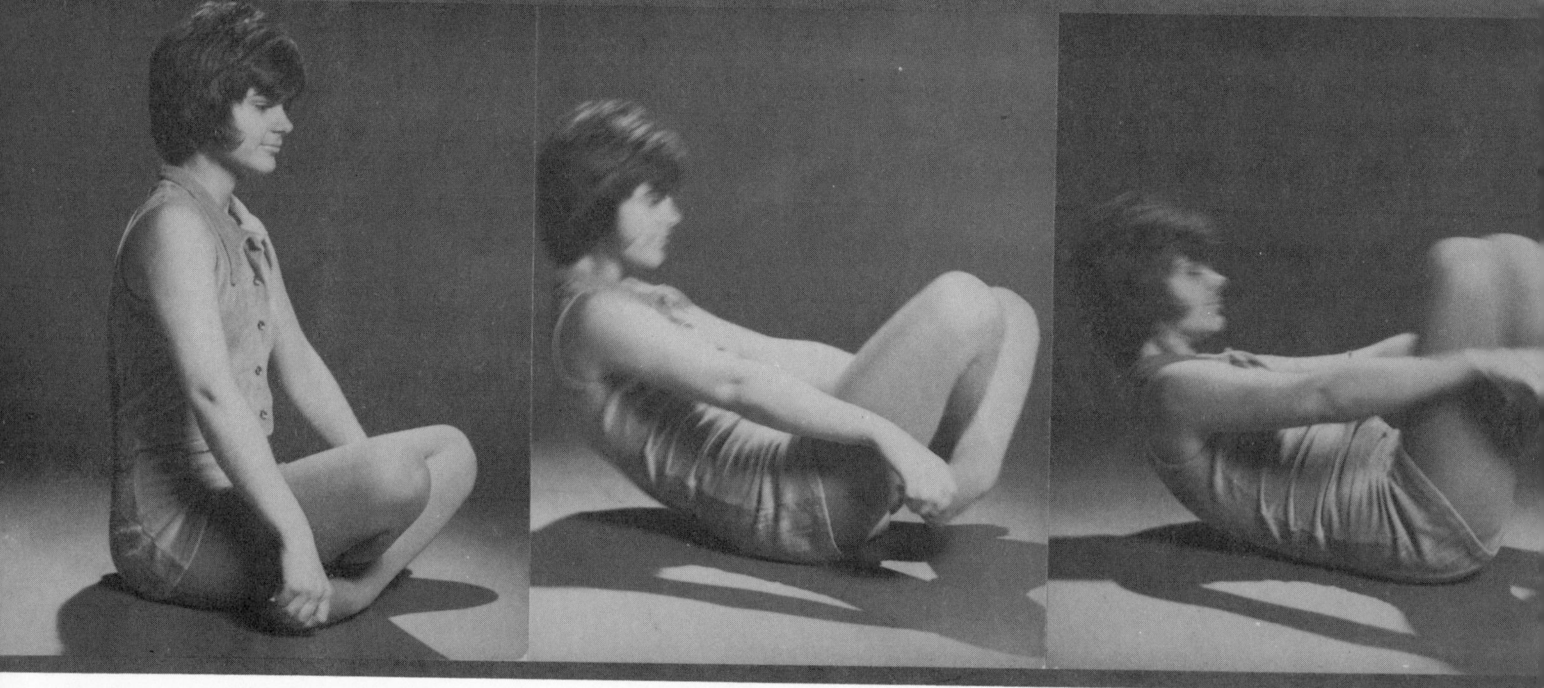

#76

The back roll

Sitting cross legged, grasp the big toes and "cinch" the legs tightly, roll backwards until the head touches the ground, repeat 12 x pulling more on one toe in order to roll "in the round."

77 THE BOW

INHALE

lace both hands close together near the center f the chest, as if holding a bow... EXHALE lowly while stretching one arm out under stress f the taut string. Return to the center starting osition and repeat with the other arm. 6X each side.

#78

Percussion on the inner thighs

Spleen, liver and kidneys meridians are stimulated by this gentle "loose wrists" massage.

79 80a

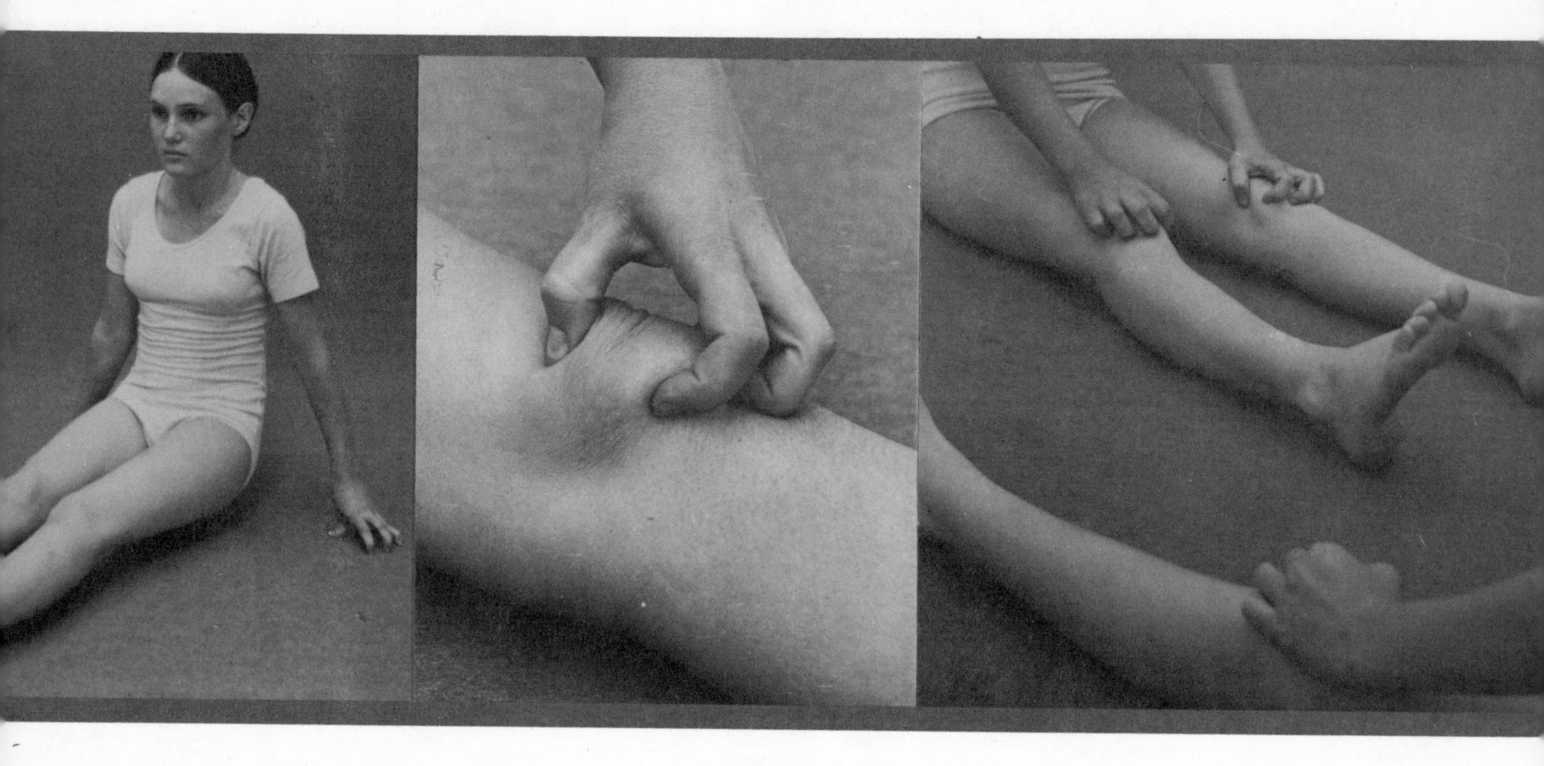

#79
Buttocks Beat

Place the finger-tips smartly on the ground on each side of the hips, raise the body quickly using only the fingertip to achieve the rise, allow the soft flesh to remain untensed.

#80A
Knee Cap rotation

With legs fully extended and feet relaxed, grasp each kneecap with hooked fingers, INHALE and begin gentle but firm rotation of the kneecaps, the left one: Clockwise while the right rotates counter clockwise.

Note: Sufferers from liver troubles and bad humored persons benefit from this massage as it relieves the congested liver and invariably brings "Good humour" to the practitioner.

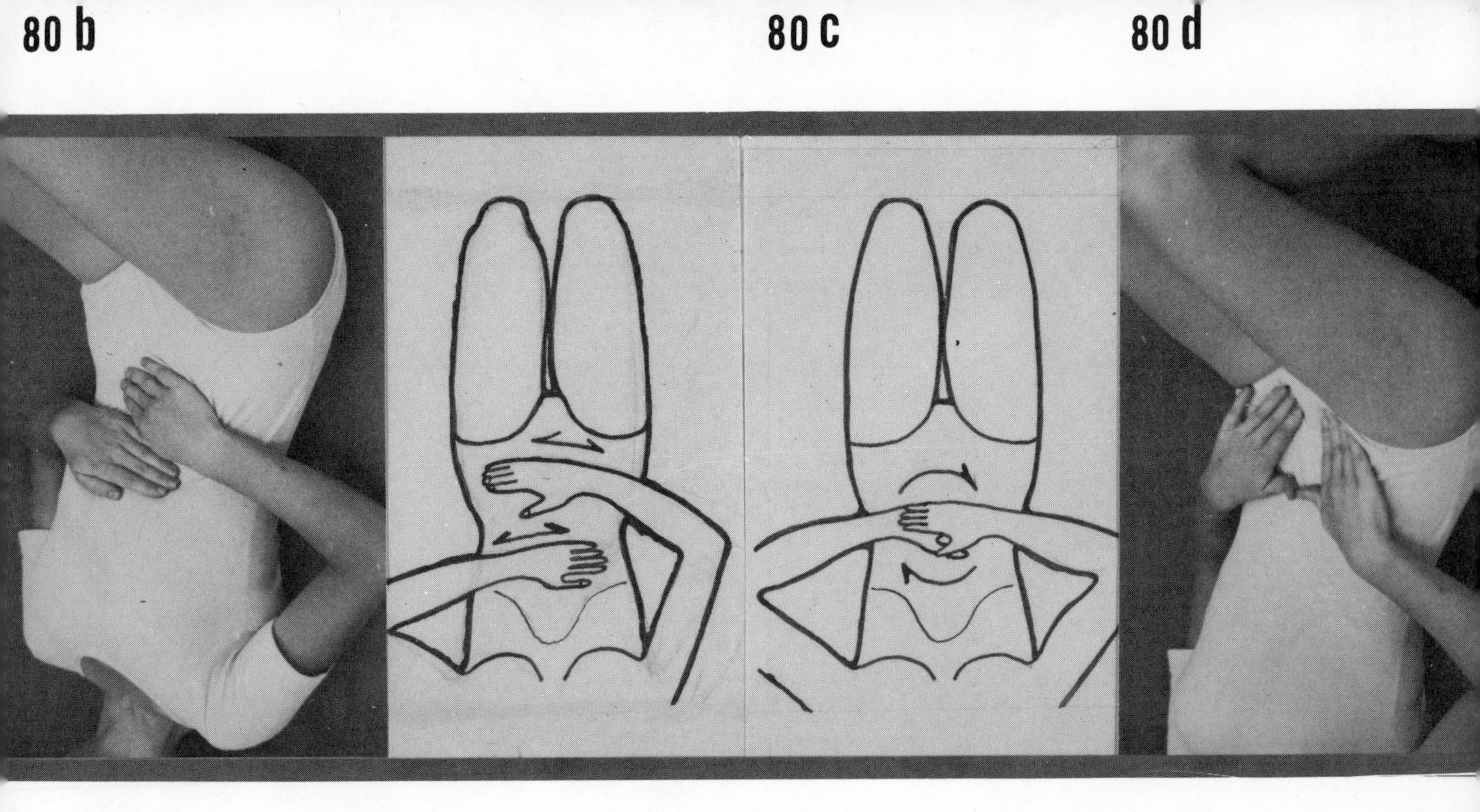

The 3/6/12 Belly Massage

First series of 3 moves
is illustrated above.

#1 - One hand above the navel and the other below,
move each hand back and forth with enough pressure
to move the soft tissues sideways.

#2 - Place one hand on top of the other, INHALE
then rotate the hands in a clockwise motion while
pressing and EXHALING slowly through the open
mouth, turn head sideways as in 90.

#3 - Place hands on each side of the groin and
pull up rhythmically while EXHALING, exert more
pressure on the upward strokes.

Repeat each of the 3 12x.

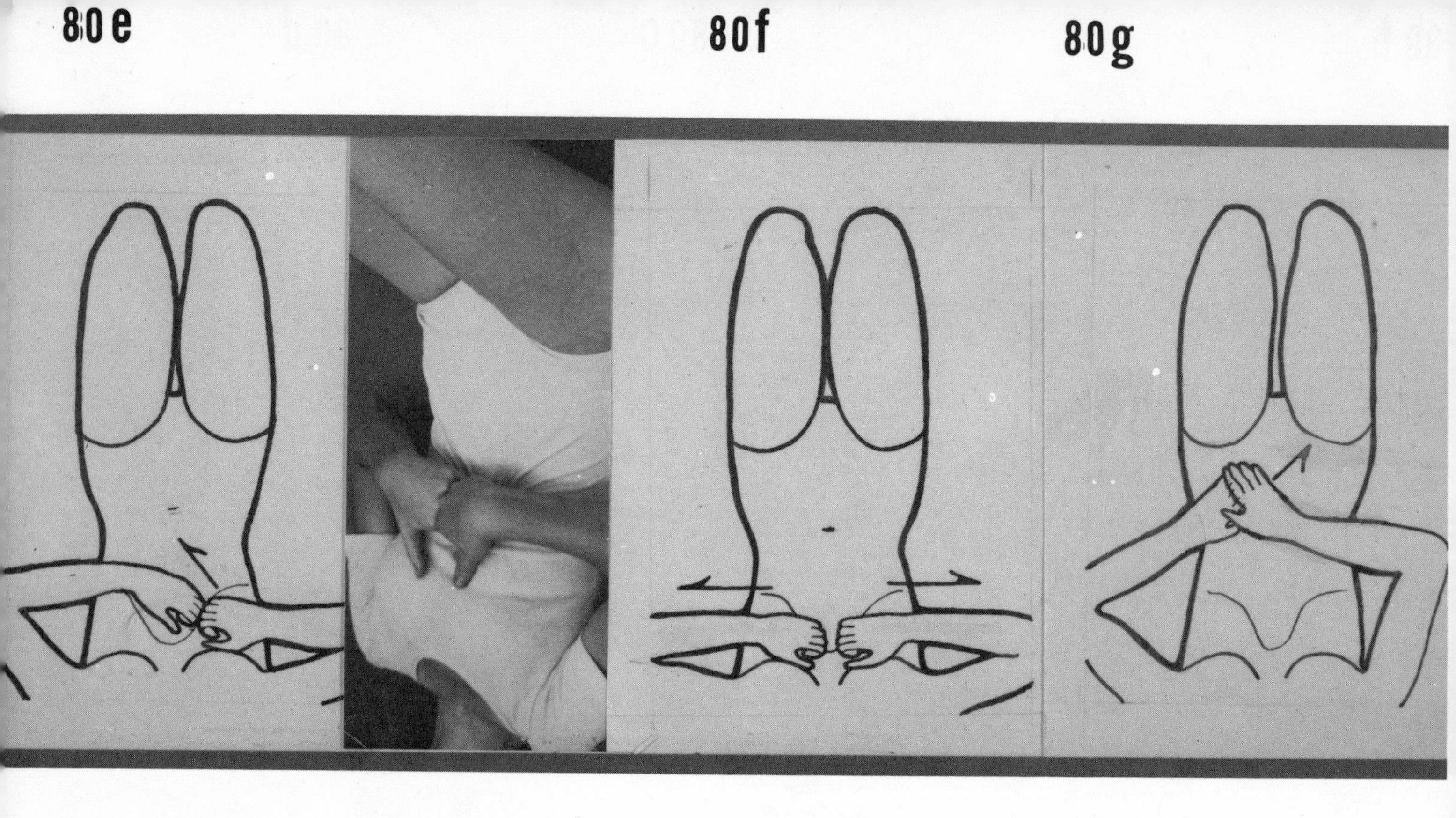

SECOND SERIES (6 positions)

The photograph shows the proper finger position for this second massage series: Hook fingers directly under the breastbone, then move to the next two areas in the median line above the navel, followed by three below. INHALE then EXHALE while increasing the finger pressure at the end of the outbreath, push in quickly and move the hands apart quickly. Repeat in each of the six positions.

THIRD SERIES
(12 positions)

Begin at lower right of the cavity perimeter. Place hand over hand and rake across toward the center of the belly, Increase pressure at the end of the outbreath

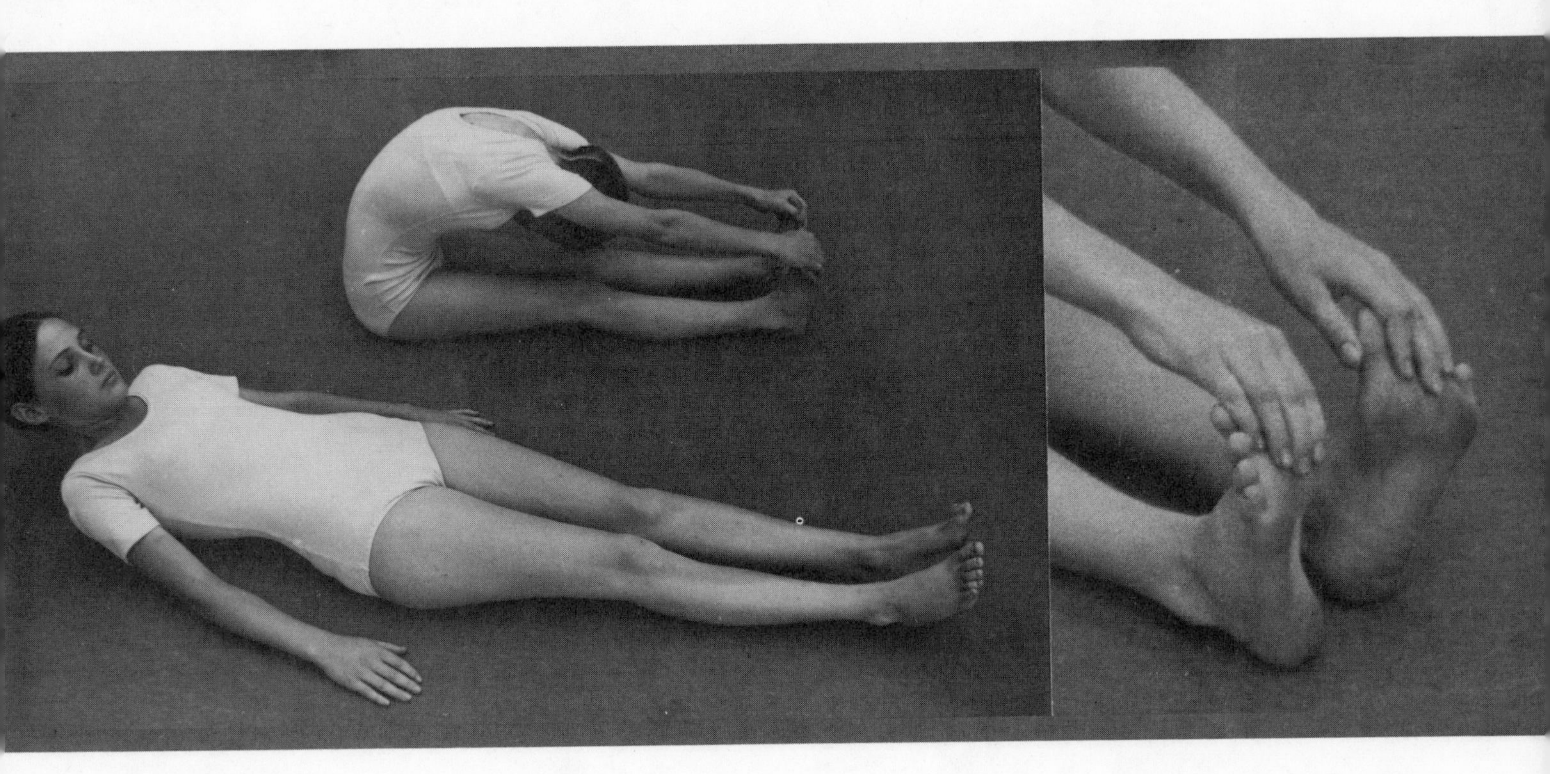

#81

REACHING FOR THE TOES

Lying supine, relaxed; breathe out and point the toes straight up.
INHALE
Keeping the knees unbent, raise the head, then the trunk and begin
to EXHALE
slowly. Bend the head lower than the arms outstretched toward the feet, attempt to place the finger tip, then the whole palm flat on the sole of the feet.

Repeat 3 x and rest.

82 83

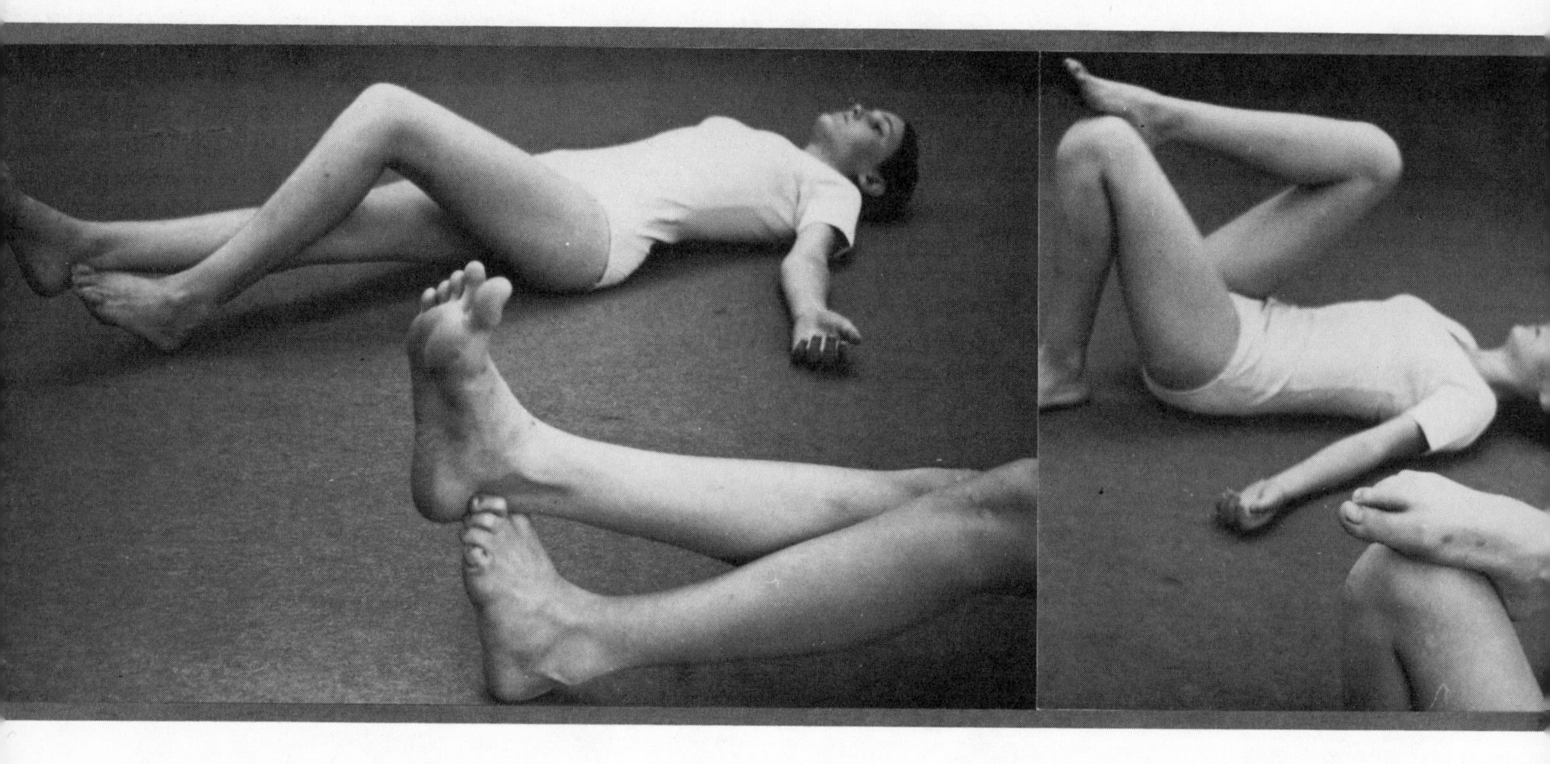

#82

STRETCHING THE ACHILLES TENDON

INHALE...

Bend the left leg slightly and open the big toe/second toe fork, place the narrow part of the heel within the fork and tighten the grip. Pull away from the body with the bent leg while EXHALING SLOWLY.

Repeat 3x, and 3x with the right leg fork.

Note: As an alternate and for more forceful expelling, turn the head to the left while exhaling...

#83

Place the arch of the sole on top of the left knee, place the left hand on top of the right knee and pull down to the ground as you EXHALE while turning the head to the right.

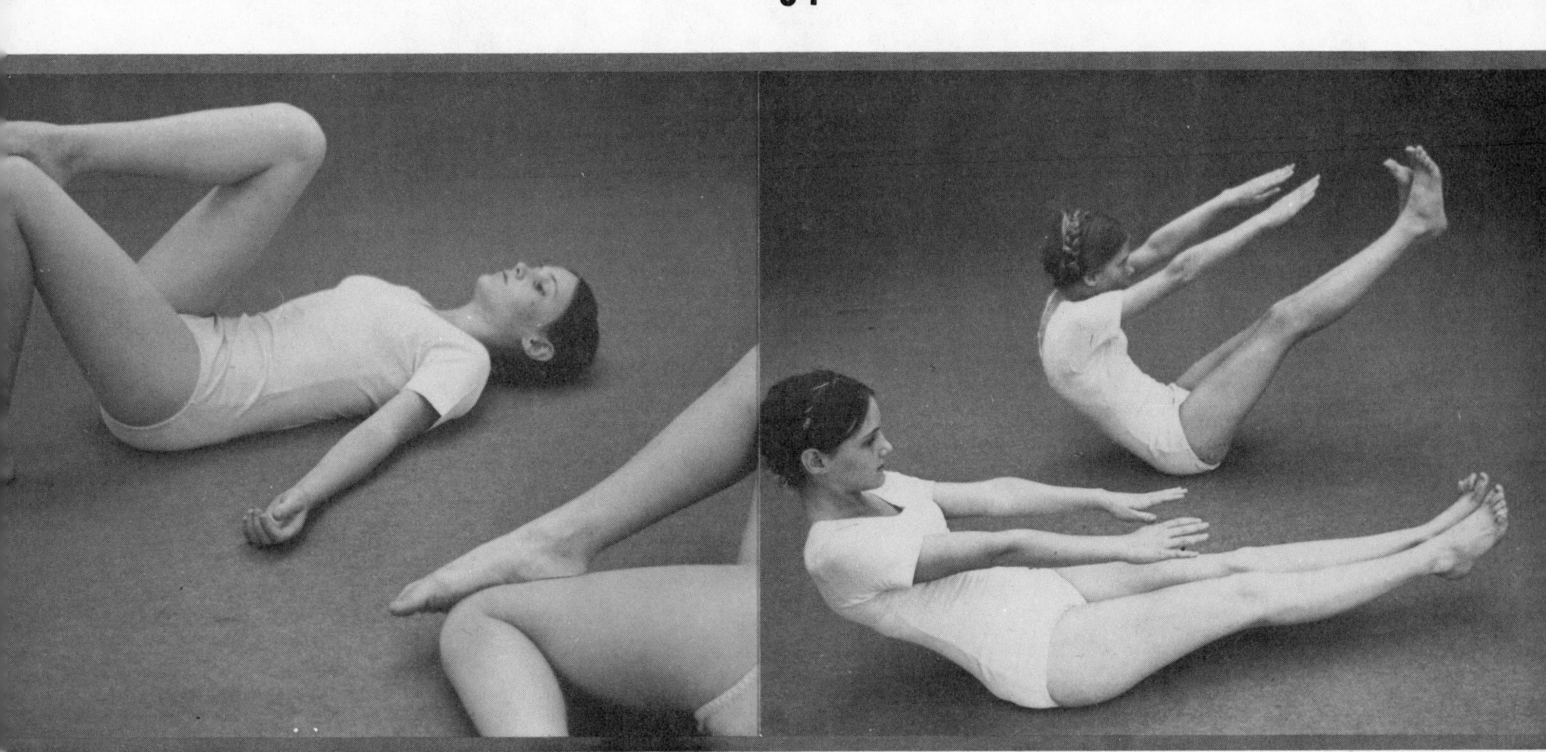

#84

Lying supine, raise both the legs
and the trunk at the same time
while EXHALING, touch the feet
with the fingertips as high
as possible.

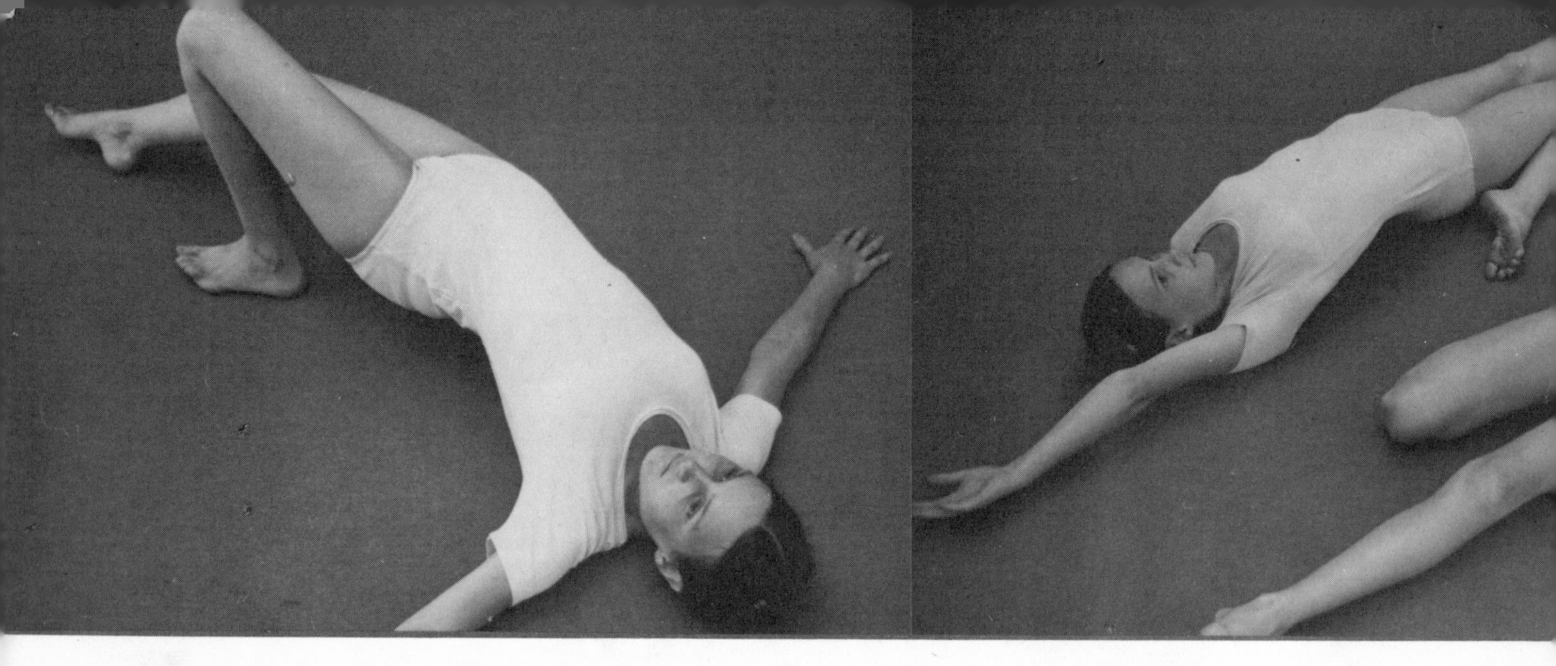

#85 TRAPEZE EXPELLER- Place one foot flat on the ground near the other knee. INHALE and lift body off without sagging. Keeping hips parallel to the ground, move the waist forcefully to one side and turn the head hard the ther way while EXHALING.

#86 THE DIAGONAL STRETCH- Bend the right leg under the thigh with the toes pointing to the head, stretch lef leg hard downward and pull the right arm straight up, mixing in the INHALED breath. Continue the down pull one side and the up pull on the other. EXHALE slowly.

#89 BACKSIDE DISCHARGE- Point the toes straight up and legs straight, clasp hands behind the neck INHALE and bend slowly down while EXHALING. 3x

#90 BACKSIDE DISCHARGE (intermediate)- Same starting position but twist the trunk as you bend forward. EXHALE and touch the left knee cap with the righ elbow, Raise the other elbow as high as possible and look up at the sky while continuing to EXHALE slowly. Repeat with the left elbow touching the right knee cap. If children cannot do this exercise, they are very ill.

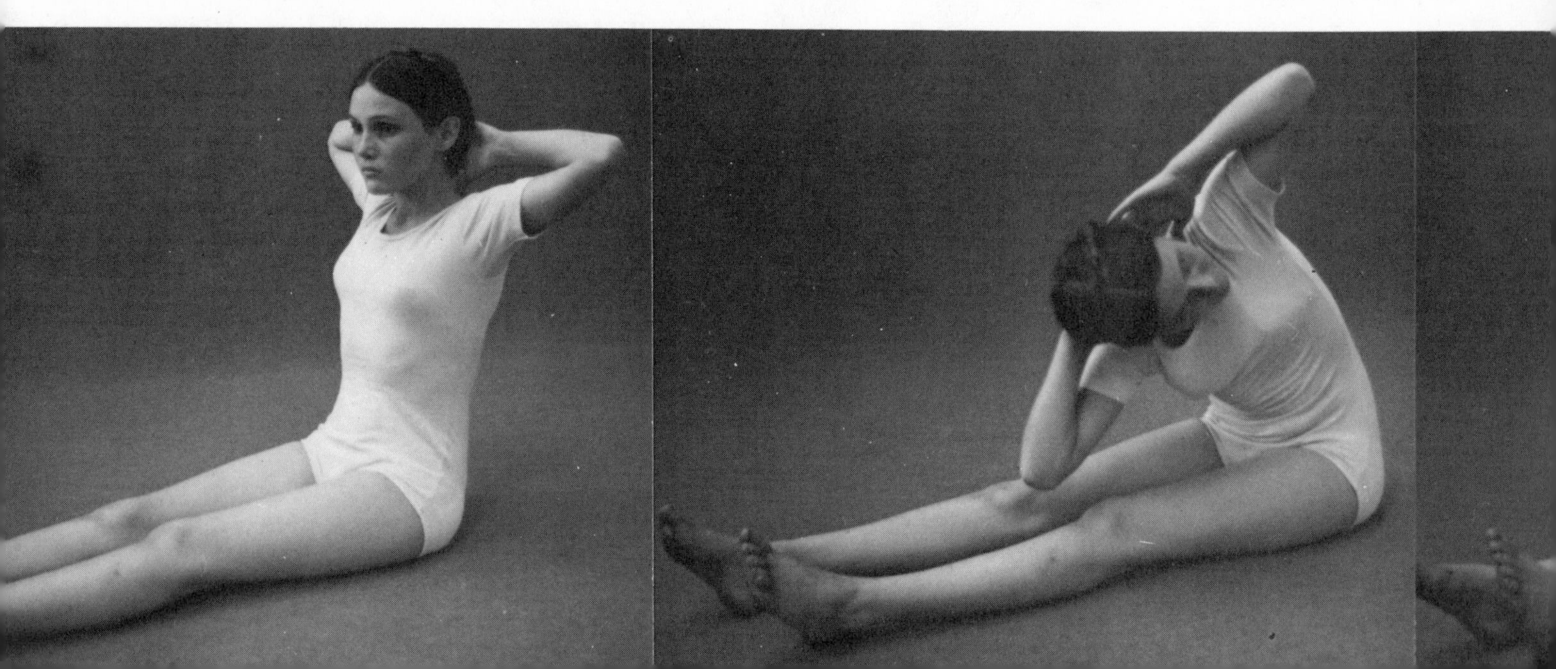

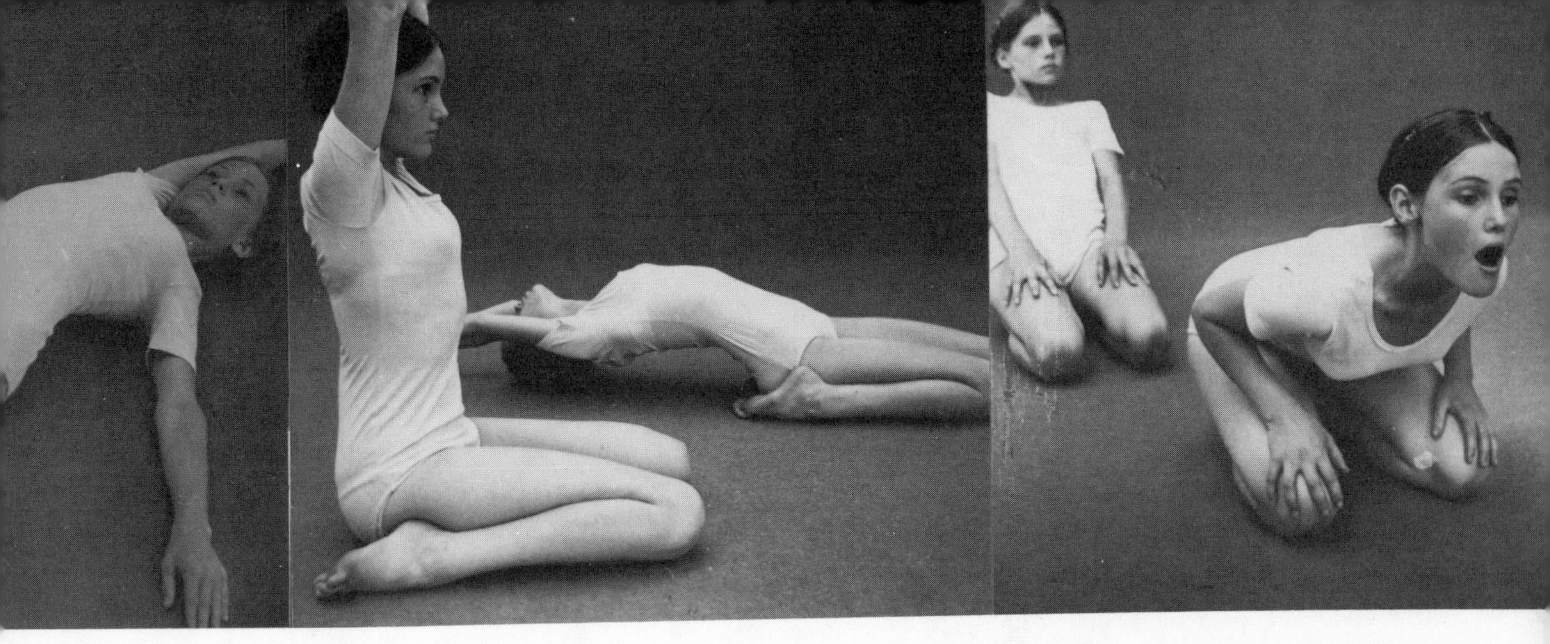

#87 YANGIZING- Sitting in seiza, trunk very straight, arms up.Open the knees wide or get someone to hold down the knees. INHALE and slowly lower backward to the ground. EXHALE and relax. Return to the starting position.

#88 THE CURIOUS HEN- Seiza position, INHALE and lean back hard, hold and mix in the breath. Slowly bend forward while EXHALING until the nose rakes the ground between the knees. Rest, breathe & repeat.

1 BACK DISCH.(advanced)
me position as at left but
ke the right elbow touch
e ground besides the left
ee. Repeat 3x each side.

#92 ROW, ROW, ROW YOUR BOAT- Grasp each foot with the fingers as shown in the first photograph. Bring one heel near the crotch area while extending the other leg out fully, bend the trunk forward and EXHALE. Begin rowing slowly and rhythmically keeping time with the breath. Touch elbow to the forward knee and head to the forearm. Strive for smoothness.

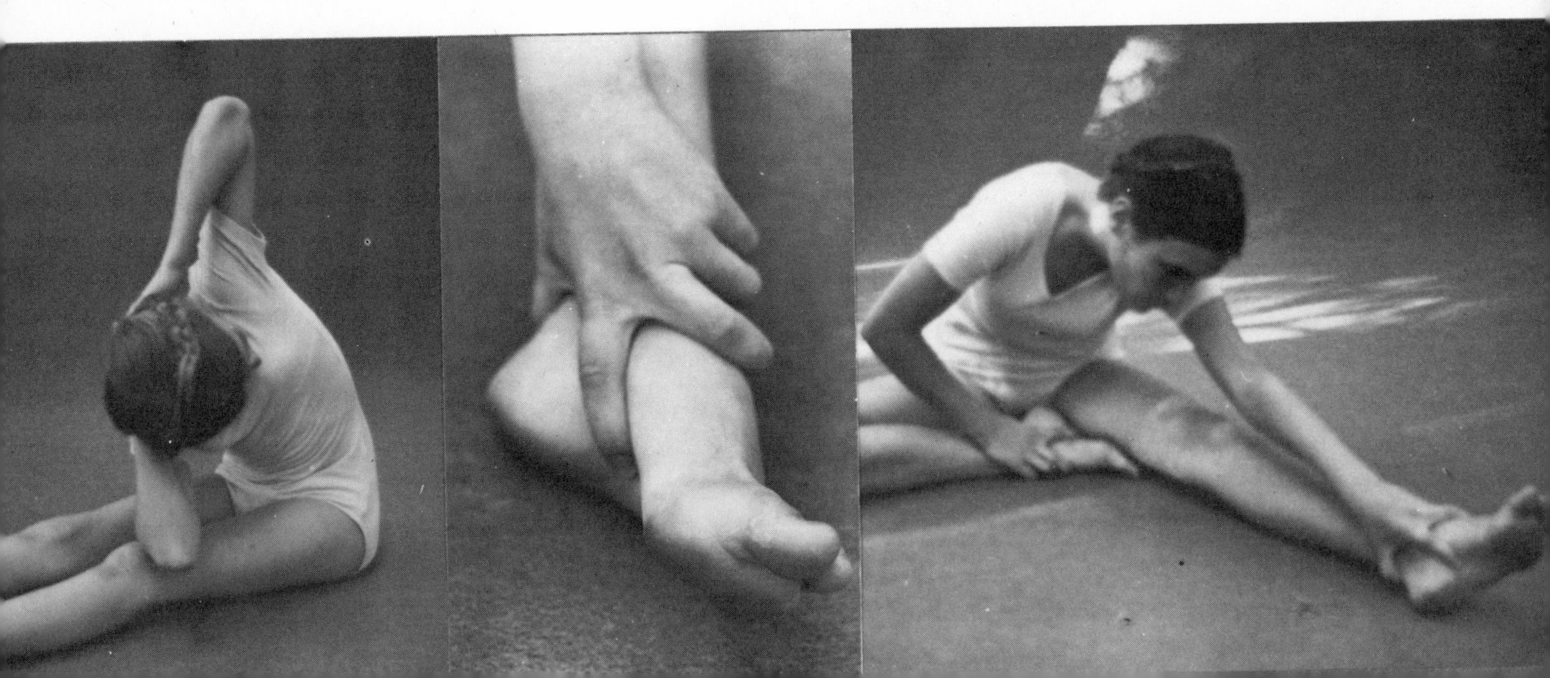

#93 and #94

DRUMMING OF THE HEEL BONES

Sitting on the ground with half bent legs, arms crossed, begin hitting with the heels gradually bringing the feet closer.

#95

Spleen stimulator

Sit with opened legs INHALE, one hand on the foot, the other pressing hard on the opposite knee,
EXHALE
as the hand slides down from the knee toward the foot, alternatively, adjust the downward movement to the breathing out.

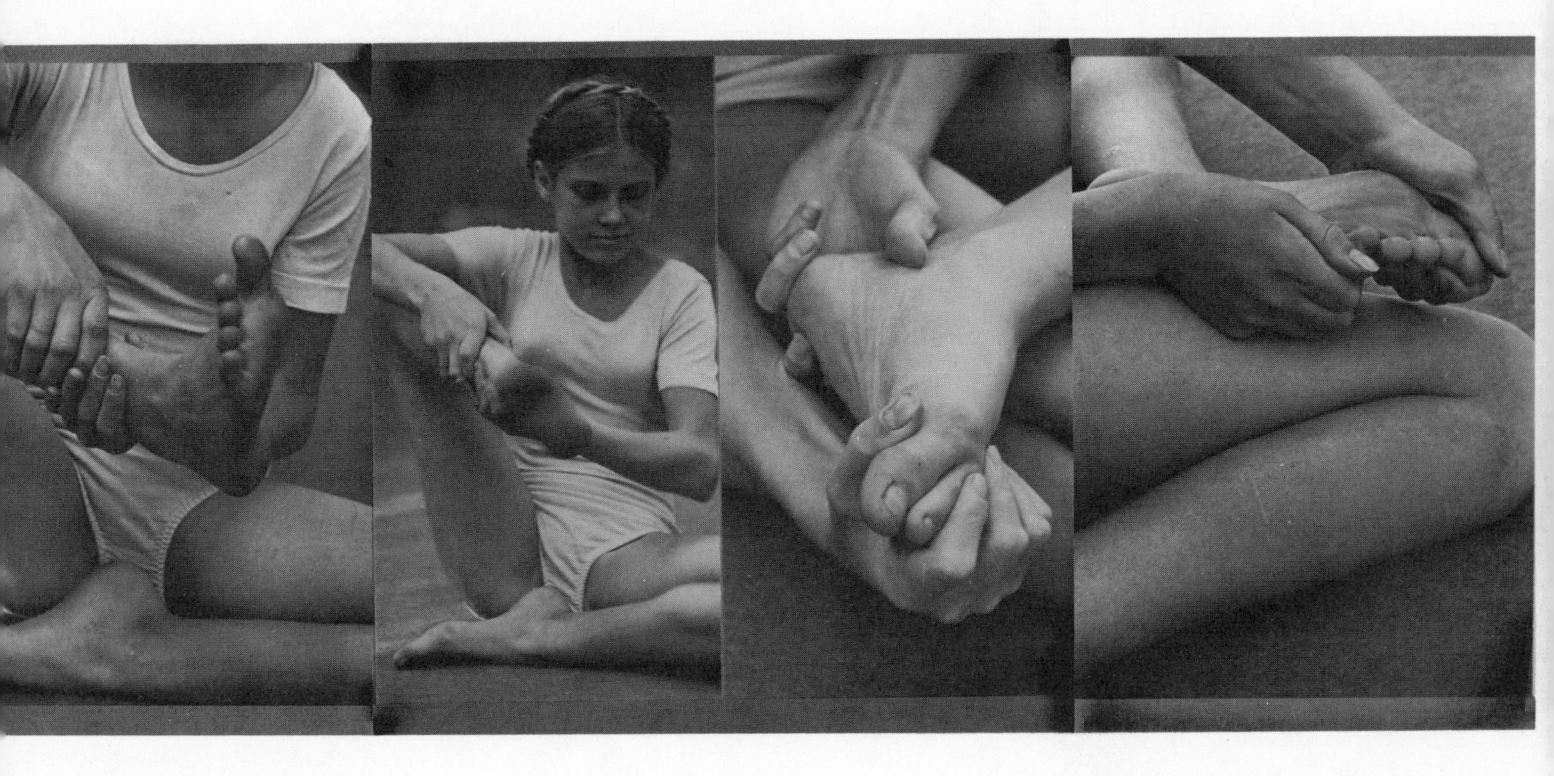

6 The Foot Shake

t on the ground with one foot
cked in, grasp the other foot
th both hands and impart hard
aking motion left and right,
y not to move the foot up and
wn, short rhythmic breathing,
ad moves to the side with open
uth outbreathing. 3x

#97

The Foot Twist

Same sitting
position but
place the foot
over the opposite
knee, grasp as
shown and twist
the end of the
foot hard EXHALE
and repeat 3x

#98

Foot Twist #2

Both hands grasp
the end of the foot
near the toes,
twist right and left
in time with the
breathing. 3x

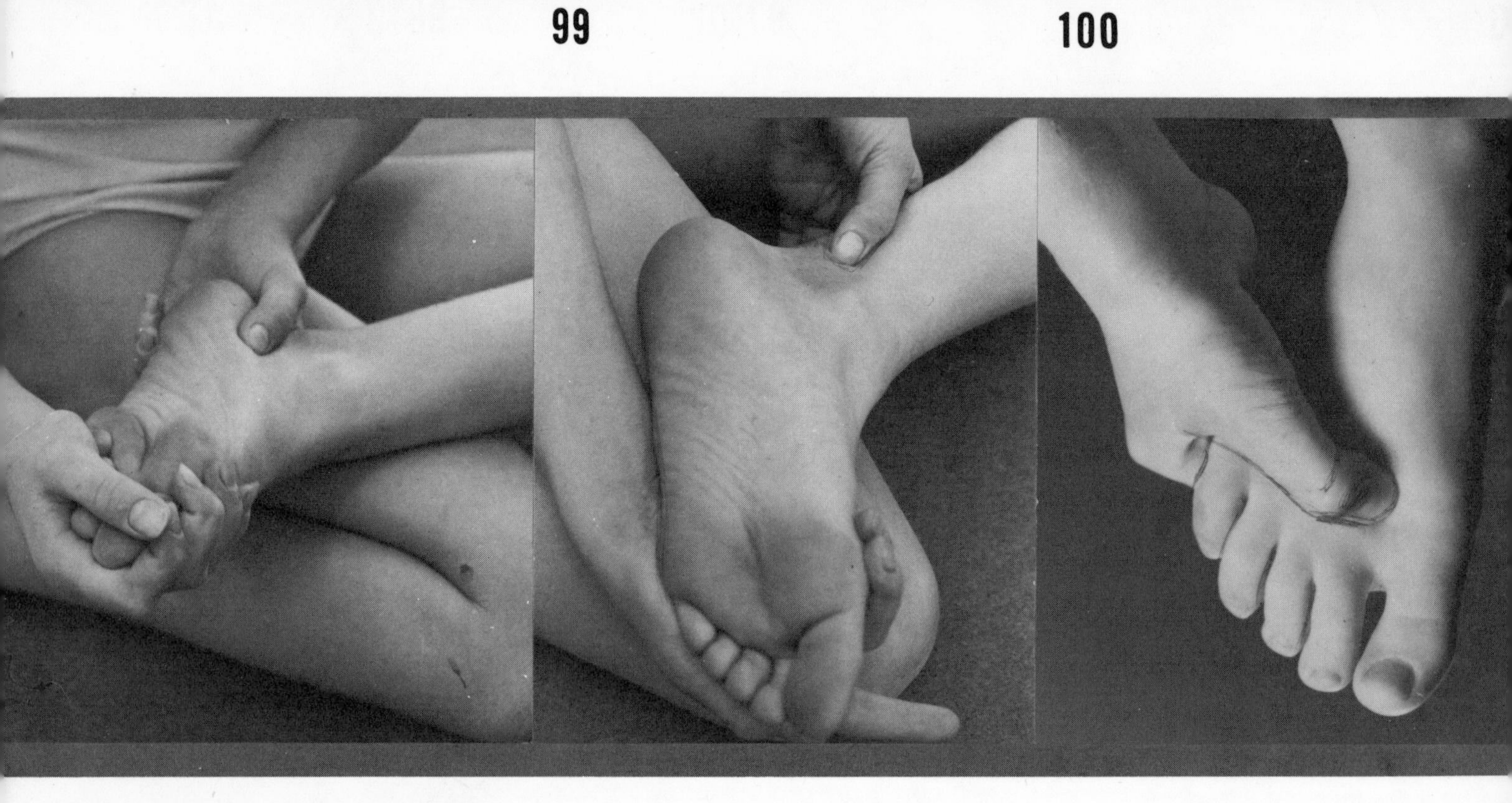

Heel in one hand as shown, toes wrapped in the other, bend the top of the foot downward in the direction of the heel. Repeat 3x

#99 Sexual Function Stimulation

Pinch hard up and down the achilles tendon Kr 4 and Bv60

#100 Press and massage deeply with the tip of the thumb at the point shown above. Lf 2 & Se 44 acupoints are affected.

101 102 103

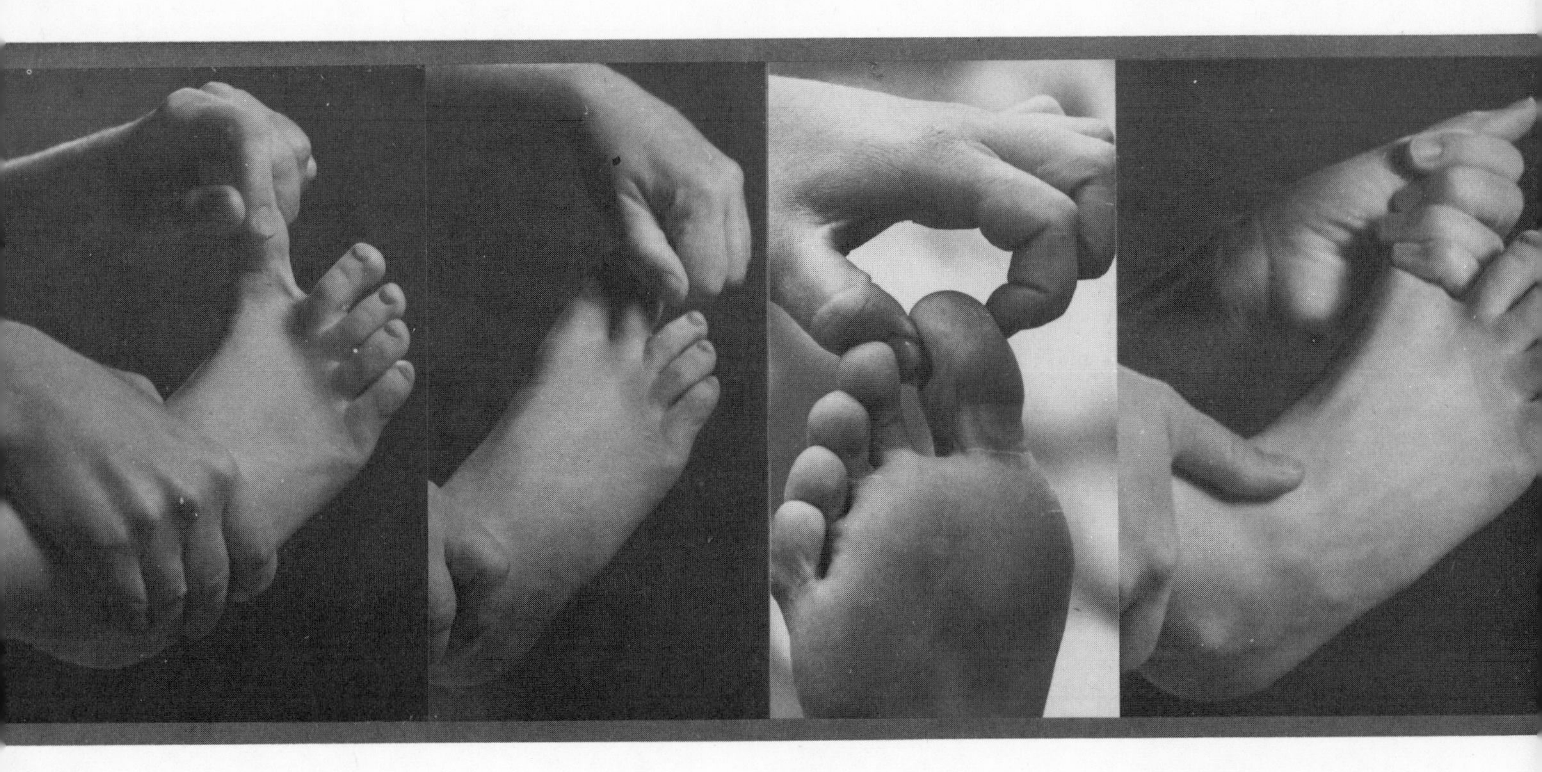

#101

Pull and rotate each toe in turn and in both directions

#102

Pinch hard at the side of each toe, dig the fingernails at the corners of the toenails

#103

Wrap the fingers around the big toes and pull away from the other toes

Sometimes called the Anti-bunion exercise.

104 105 106

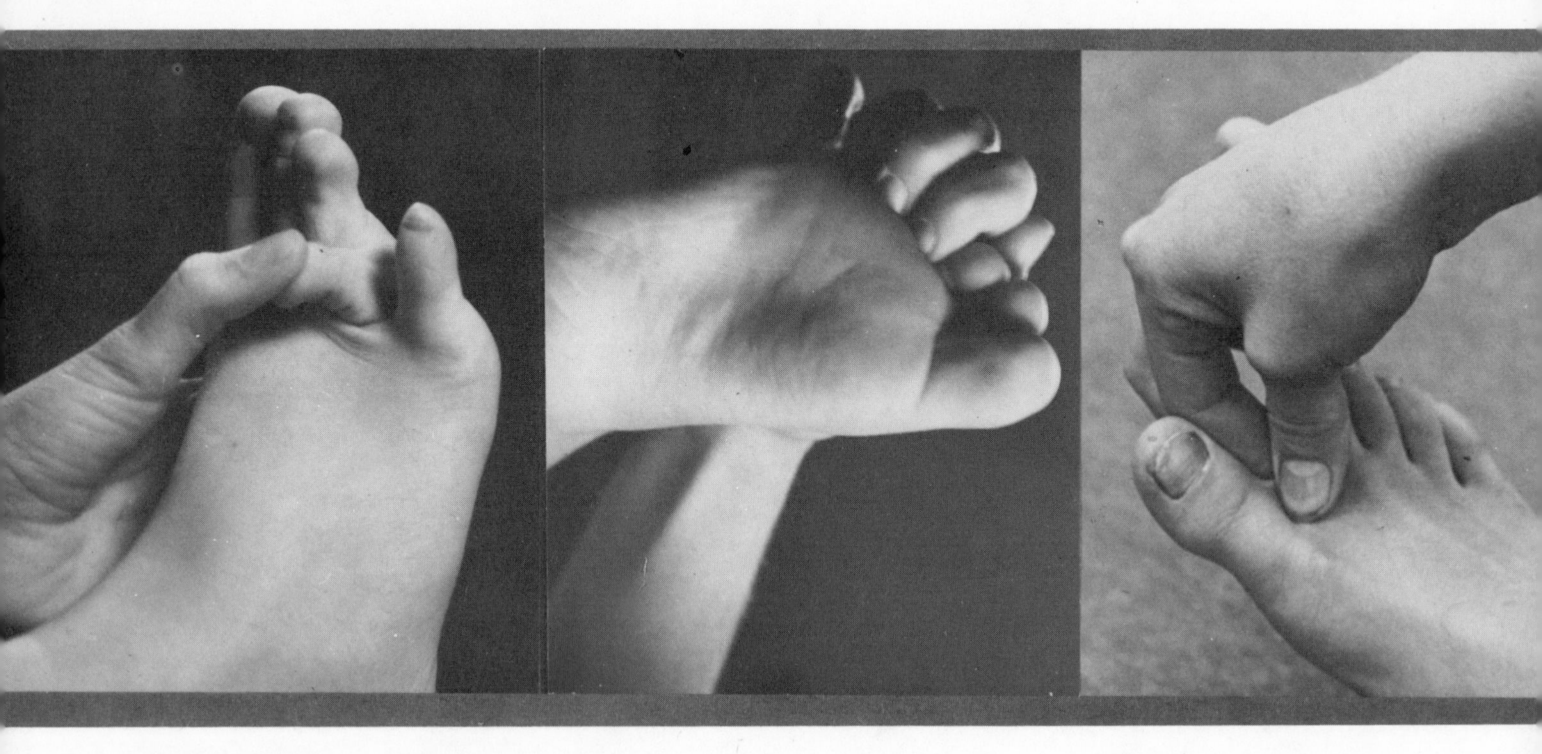

#104 Bend each toe upward and try to make it touch the top of the foot, also rub the finger hard in between each toe.

#105
Push the fingertips hard into the hollow at the base of each toe as shown above. One of the strongest inductive massage known. (See pg.30)

#106
Pinch the flesh web between each toe, clean out the accumulated toxins

Pain indicates excesses and poisons.

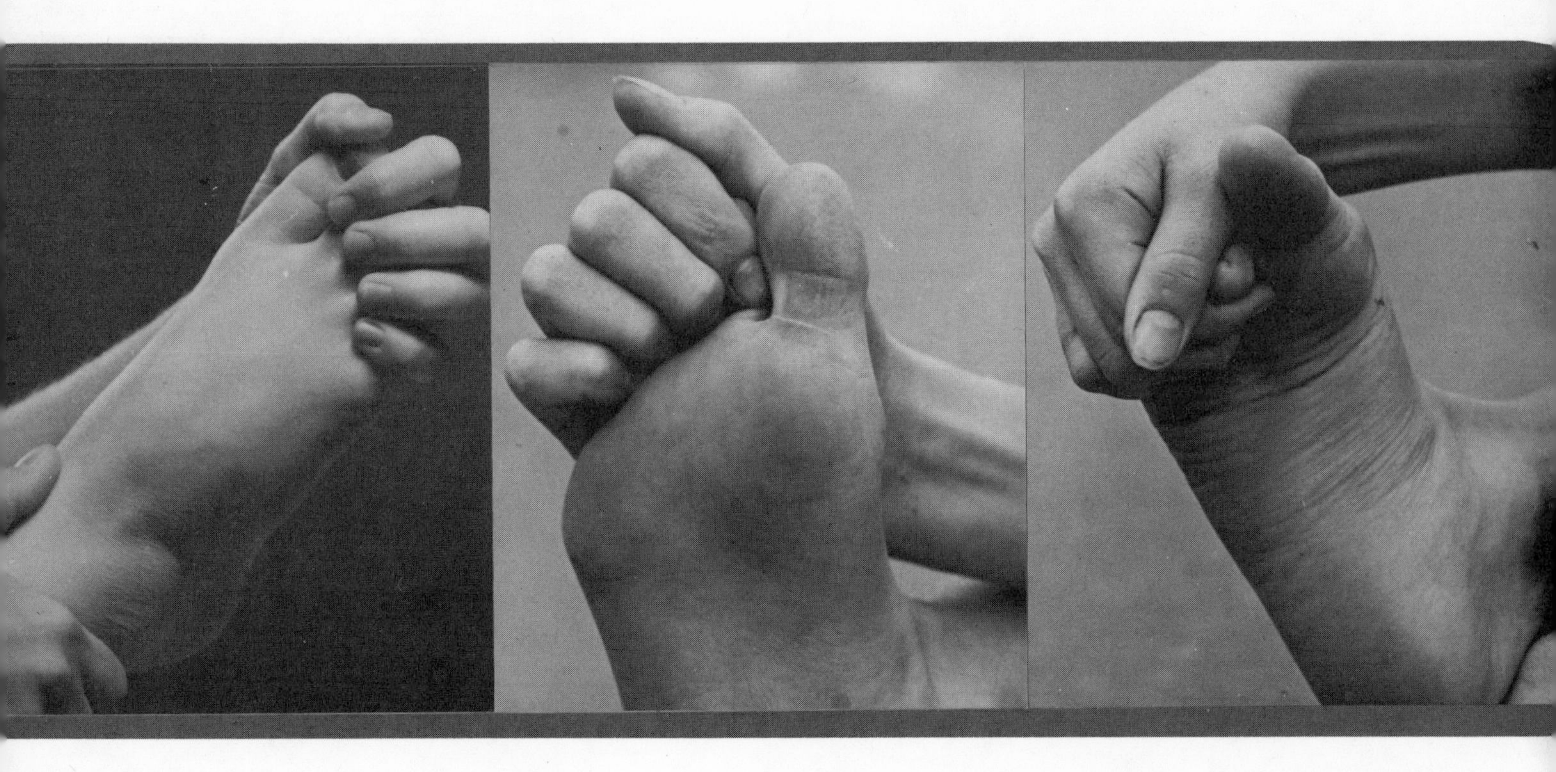

#107

Straighten the toes

With the palm of the hand flat on the sole of the foot, relax and unbend the toes, move them right and left rock them to and fro.

#108

Bend the toes downward

Grasp the four toes as shown, (fingertips could end at a lower point) INHALE and channel the breath down into the toes, straighten, stretch and flatten the toes...

Continued from the photo at the left...

With an upward flick of the wrist, quickly bend the toes under. Some cracking (soft or loud) might occur indicating release of toxin deposits.

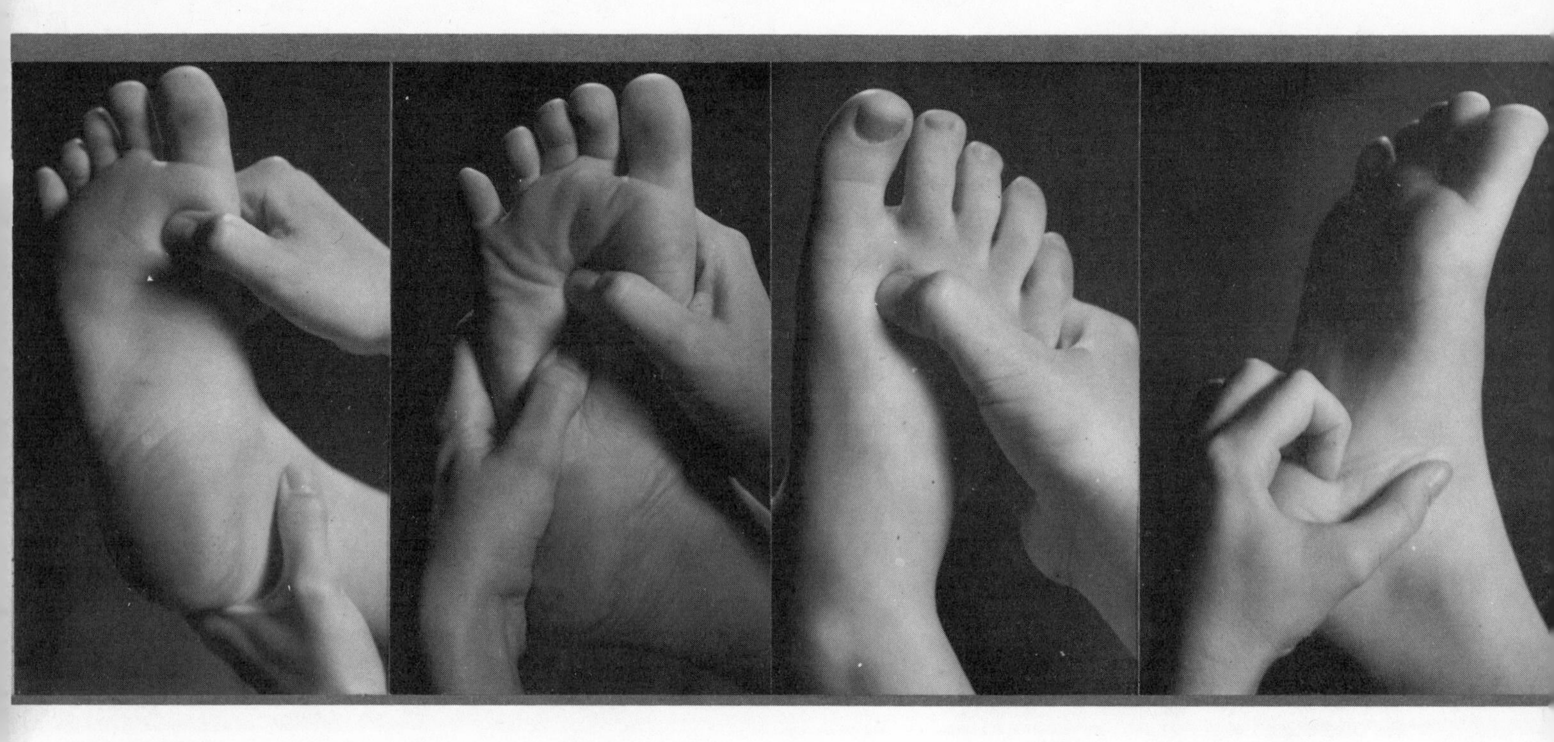

#109

Fingertip effect a deep massage all over the sole and the surface of the feet, deep kneading with the thumbs of both hands, bending the foot inward and wrapping the soles around the fingers as you massage

#110

Hold the heel in the palm of the hand, dig in all four fingers into the area just above the heel bone.

111

112

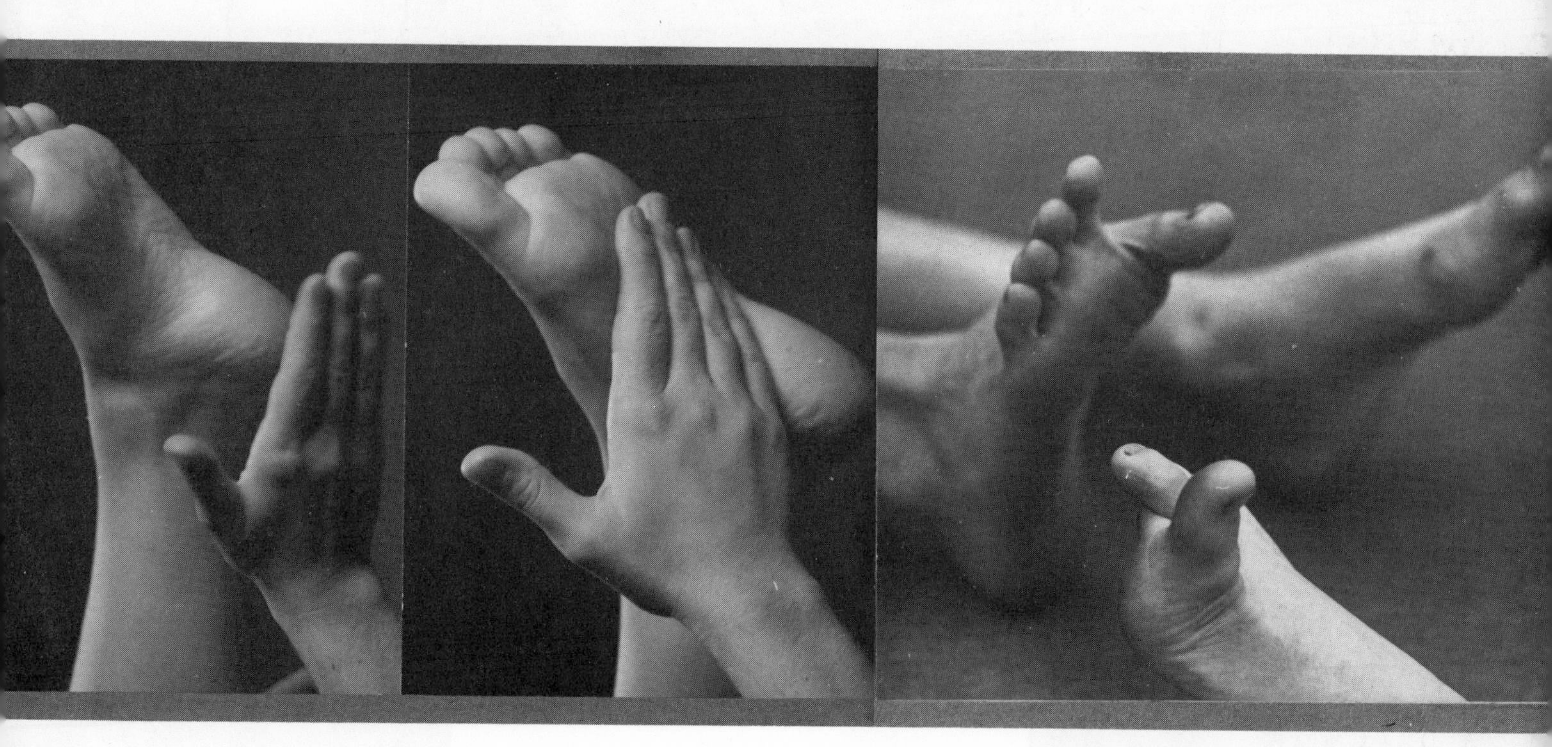

111

lapping the sole of the feet

oud resounding clapping on
he entire surface of the sole
elps the circulation of Ki. 50X

#112

Flicking the toes in opposite directions.

Toes quickly regain their flexibility and suppleness. Alternatively bend the big toes forward while bending the other toes backward, retrain their lost muscle memory by hand at first if necessary. 100X

FEB 16 1984

Lithographed by
WASHINGTON LITHOGRAPH CO., INC.
Los Angeles, California